GEORGE HOUSE

HERITAGE BED & BREAKFAST

Kitchen Recipes

Library and Archives Canada Cataloguing in Publication

Warren, Todd, 1969-
George House Heritage Bed and Breakfast : kitchen recipes / Todd Warren and Dale Cameron.

Includes index.
A taste tempting cookbook of more than 300 tried, tested and true recipes; including many Newfoundland favourites and old time classic recipes as well as many stories, and timeless cooking tips.
ISBN 978-1-897317-62-4

1. Cookery, Canadian--Newfoundland style. 2. Cookery--Newfoundland and Labrador. 3. George House Heritage Bed and Breakfast. I. Cameron, Dale, 1968- II. George House Heritage Bed and Breakfast III. Title.

TX715.6.W354 2010 641.509718 C2010-902959-3

PRINTED IN CANADA

This text of this book is printed on Ancient Forest Friendly paper, FSC certified, that is chlorine-free and 100% post-consumer waste.

Cover Design: Adam Freake
Interior Layout: Albert Taylor

FLANKER PRESS LTD.
PO BOX 2522, STATION C
ST. JOHN'S, NL
CANADA

TELEPHONE: (709) 739-4477 FAX: (709) 739-4420 TOLL-FREE: 1-866-739-4420

WWW.FLANKERPRESS.COM

14 13 12 11 10 1 2 3 4 5 6 7 8

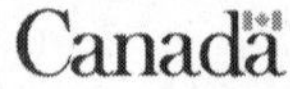

Canada Council for the Arts Conseil des Arts du Canada

We acknowledge the financial support of the Government of Canada through the Book Publishing Industry Development Program (BPIDP) for our publishing activities; the Canada Council for the Arts which last year invested $20.1 million in writing and publishing throughout Canada; the Government of Newfoundland and Labrador, Department of Tourism, Culture and Recreation.

GEORGE HOUSE

HERITAGE BED & BREAKFAST

Kitchen Recipes

A taste-tempting cookbook of more than 300 tried, tested and true recipes including many Newfoundland favourites and old-time classic recipes as well as many guest comments, Newfoundland trivia, and timeless cooking tips

TODD WARREN and DALE CAMERON

FLANKER PRESS
ST. JOHN'S
2010

We dedicate this book
to our mothers

and

our family and friends
for their encouragement

and

to the countless guests
who have always asked:

"Can I have your recipe for . . ."

Acknowledgements

We would like to thank all of those guests, family members and friends who collected recipes, passed them along with their compliments and for those whom we asked, "Could you try this dish? We want your opinion as we are making a cookbook and want to know what you think."

A special note of acknowledgement goes out to Todd's mother, Marina Warren, for taking the time to write down her recipes that she keeps in her head, to our valued staff members Doris Garland for sharing her fish recipe, Tammy Boyer for her Hopeall coffee cake, Ruby Legge (who we affectionately call Aunt Ruby) for her Aunt Emily's Cake, and the many others who contributed their cherished recipes.

"The Journey," by Dale Cameron

My first memories of being in a kitchen were about 37 years ago as I assisted my mom as her "Cookie." She would say that she was the cook and therefore I was the "Cookie." Of course I was only about four years old at the time and my duties usually included scraping a bowl or occasionally stirring the batter.

My mother was an exceptional, self-taught baker and she would produce wonderful breads, biscuits, muffins, sweets, and pies. She made homemade jams, jellies, and pickles. My food memories as a child include homemade applesauce, pumpkin jelly, warm tea biscuits, homemade lemon meringue pie, oatmeal coffee cake, and her wonderful brown bread with raisins.

Due to our family relocating east, as a child I had to wait for an additional year to start elementary school, and there wasn't kindergarten at the time, so I spent lots of time in the kitchen with my mom helping her – or so I thought I was, when actually she was just keeping an eye on me and trying to keep me out of mischief. She would allow me to assist her in stirring, measuring, and scraping the bowls in exchange for me assisting with the dishes. While I detested doing the dishes, I thought the task was worth the fun of helping.

My mom had a stove with two oven doors and she would leave them open to warm up the kitchen after she had removed whatever she had baked that day. As children we were happy to have homemade cookies in our school lunches, and treats after we arrived home from school. Mom would have prepared our evening meal and, as my dad was a "meat and potatoes" man, she always had traditional basics like meat loaf, roast beef, shepherd's pie, corn chowder, beef stew, pork chop skillet bake, and boiled dinner.

At some point in my childhood, my mom began to work outside of the home, and while she worked evenings she still continued to bake and cook for the family. So I substituted my on-the-job training in the kitchen with watching the action on a variety of television cooking shows. We didn't have cable TV in the 1970s and early 1980s and only had two English television channels, channels 2 and 7, and channel 11 was French-language television.

I can vividly remember watching Ruth Frames on *What's Cooking*, Bruno Gerussi with *Celebrity Cooks*, Graham Kerr on *The Galloping Gourmet* reruns, Stephen Yan on *Wok With Yan* and *Yan Can Cook*, and two special favourites were James Barber's *The Urban Peasant* and Madame Jehane Ben-

oit on *The Young Chefs*. I remember watching to see what ingredients they were going to use, how they would use them, and wish I could be there in their TV kitchen to assist and taste along with them.

After the death of my mother I remember trying to recreate her signature dishes and I realized that while anyone can make a dish from a recipe, each cook adds his own personality to the dish. And, while I've never been able to fully recreate her dishes, I've come close and, as all cooks do, I've added my own personality to it.

Over the past number of years I've taken a few night school courses in food preparation that have continued my interest in cooking. I began clipping recipes and trying them and sharing recipes with friends. I've always enjoyed making dishes to bring to potluck parties – and once remember making a few hundred egg rolls for a retirement party in Renfrew, Ontario. My house smelled of cooked cabbage for weeks afterward.

Cookbooks offer lots of inspiration to an eager cook, and I think of a cookbook as a great novel – something to be read from cover to cover. I've collected hundreds of cookbooks over the years and always enjoy reading them and choosing recipes to try. Sometimes they turn out just like the photo in the book, and other times they don't. Often I'll include the ingredients the way a recipe calls for it to be prepared, and then the next time I make it I'll adjust the recipe to make it my own.

Several years ago I thought about writing a cookbook, and due to time restraints and lack of focus it never happened. Then, two years ago, Todd and I were working at the bed and breakfast, and guests asked us for the recipe for a dish that we had prepared. I wrote it out for them and the guests said, "Why don't you make a cookbook, as I'm sure we're not the first guests to ask for this recipe?" Later that night, after the kitchen was closed, we sat with a glass of wine and said, "Why don't we?" And thus the concept began.

This cookbook includes many recipes that we have tried over the years, ones that were given to us by family, friends, and from our travels. The recipes are straightforward and use commonly found ingredients and kitchen tools so that a basic cook or baker can easily create anything from the book.

So, when I think about this cookbook I think of the days I had as a child in the kitchen with my mom, those afternoons sitting on the living-room carpet watching Ruth, Bruno, Graham, Steven, James, and Madame Benoit on a small black and white television with rabbit ears, and all the different ways in which food was created are some of the best memories in my life.

Dale Cameron

"Inspiration," by Todd Warren

I often wonder what our ancestors ate when they first arrived on the shores that are now Newfoundland and Labrador.

I have many fond memories that revolve around food and I often remember being a child and anxiously awaiting our Christmas dinner, and days in the summer when I longed for fresh fish. There were those days when I would rush home from school and watch my mother bake cakes and cookies and cook our evening meals. I would stay by her side to watch and help her prepare dinner and provide my young commentary as I tasted her soups and nibbled on pastry.

At the age of ten I began experimenting with how food was made. I would wait until there was a time when my parents and siblings were out of the house and I would seek a chocolate cake mix from the kitchen cupboard and I would make the batter according to the directions. Only about half of the batter would make it into a pan and the oven, as the other half would have been devoured by me in the process of mixing the batter. Then the only thing left to do would be to eat the baked cake once it was iced to ensure all morsels were gone so there was no evidence I was tampering in Mom's kitchen.

I don't know if this was any indication of my first love of sweet foods or the beginning of my interest in the kitchen and its many wonders.

This cookbook has been a dream of mine for many years. Since I first opened Inn By The Bay and subsequently opened George House Heritage Bed & Breakfast, our guests would frequently ask, "How did you make this," "Where did you go to cooking school," "Can I have this recipe," and, "Have you ever thought of making a cookbook?" Although I had no formal training in cooking I would smile and say, "I cook using recipes and my imagination and just taste as I go."

At the time I was in school for my formal training in the hospitality industry I was offered a job by a hotel in St. John's as a waiter part-time and part-time front desk clerk. This gave me a wonderful introduction to the hospitality industry as well as its demands. I took that opportunity to ask the chefs why they put certain items on the menu, inquired as to how they would make a certain dish, and learned all I could on the job. Eventually, my career advanced and I moved from one hotel property to another, and I was always pleased to assist the kitchen when large banquets were held, and I had the coveted role of "Gravy Boy" at the end of the production line, ensuring the plate was perfect before being served.

In the early, entrepreneurial days of my foray into the bed and breakfast business, I would wonder, *How will I prepare the food for the guests?* Would I only prepare breakfast or should I include lunch and perhaps even evening dinner? So I simply began by preparing basic foods, continued to search for new recipes to try, and picked up cookbooks that were interesting, and I changed recipes to reflect my own cooking personality.

During the slow times of the year I watched classic cooking shows such as *Cooking with Julia Child* and Martha Stewart's show and found inspiration. Then I began to notice, as I watched other television shows, that my attention was on the food they served and ate, and not on the plot at all. I was hooked.

Over the past 13 yeas in the bed and breakfast business I have tried to count the sheer number of guests who have enjoyed breakfast, evening dinner and even my two attempts at attracting a local lunch crowd. I've held charity dinner events, hosted dozens of Christmas parties, and even made homemade preserves and sold them.

My greatest accomplishments, in addition to our guests commenting favourably about their dining experience, have been the many mentions of my food in established travel guides such as *Fodor's*, *Frommers*, *Lonely Planet*, *Moon*, and of course *Where to Eat in Canada* over the past several years.

The food from this little bed and breakfast in Dildo, Newfoundland, has been highlighted in many other publications such as *The National Post*, *The Globe & Mail*, *The New York Times*, *The Toronto Star*, *The Toronto Sun*, *The UK Independent*, and it's been recognized on many websites and even a few television programs.

It has been with the assistance of my partner Dale and his love of food as well, that this cookbook has gone from a dream to a reality. Our life includes wonderful memories and as always they are peppered with wonderful adventures in food. When we recall a trip or memory we are often caught reminiscing, saying, "Remember that is where we ate the . . . and had the . . ."

In closing, I hope you enjoy flipping through these pages and savouring the many gifts they have to offer.

Todd Warren

About recipes from the kitchen of the George House Heritage Bed & Breakfast

At bed and breakfasts and country inns, cooking takes on a whole new dimension where guests make memories of their most favourite dishes, and now you can create this at home with *George House Heritage Bed & Breakfast Kitchen Recipes.*

Continuing in the tradition of hospitality, Newfoundland innkeepers Todd Warren and Dale Cameron offer classic recipes that are time-tested and true. For over 20 years they have cooked and enjoyed presenting their food for family, friends, and guests at their bed and breakfast and inn.

George House Heritage Bed & Breakfast Kitchen Recipes celebrates the 125-year history of the George House in 2010 as a historic landmark in Dildo, Newfoundland, and Todd and Dale's cookbook showcases traditional Newfoundland favourites as well as many personal recipes that guests have asked for over the years. As you leaf through the pages of this cookbook you will have an adventure in cooking, and it will be as rewarding to read as it will be to use as your handbook in the kitchen.

In preparing this cookbook, it was not the authors' aim to present the art of cooking from a professional standpoint, but rather to give, in a very simple and clear manner, the art of cooking and baking to the everyday person. You don't have to be a five-star cook to enjoy this five-star bed and breakfast's cookbook.

This collection of recipes includes a variety of tasty, simple-to-make dishes that include step-by-step instructions and utilize common ingredients. In this cookbook, the authors share their recipes along with guest comments and timeless, helpful kitchen hints and tips. From beginner cooks to the advanced, there is something for everyone.

If you are from Newfoundland, the authors hope this book will encourage you to try these recipes. If you are from away, they hope that you will try the exciting culinary world that is presented in this book.

Recipes include: appetizers, breakfasts, snacks, breads, biscuits, muffins, soups, chowders, stews, vegetables and sides, main dishes, sauces and gravies, timeless Newfoundland favourites, desserts and sweets – including cookies, cakes, and pies – as well as beverages.

Contents

STARTERS

BREAKFASTS & SNACKS

BISCUITS

BREADS

MUFFINS

SALADS

SOUPS & CHOWDERS

STEWS

VEGETABLES & SIDE DISHES

BEEF

FISH & SHELLFISH

PASTAS

PORK

POULTRY

GRAVIES

SAUCES

TIMELESS NEWFOUNDLAND FAVOURITES

CAKES

COOKIES

PIES

SWEETS

COCKTAILS

MARTINIS

SPIRITED COFFEES

A Recipe Poem

All women are possessed of a common disease
And that's clipping out various recipes.

These collections grow to a formidable number
With dishes to serve both winter and summer.

What happens then, when they build up to a pile?
Do they put them away in a neat little file? No!

They just dump them all in a box or drawer
And go on collecting and clipping some more.

Then the time comes along when they want to use
That nifty concoction from The Daily News.

Their mouths water with thoughts of that dish
And they drive right in to hunt and to fish.

But the hours go by in the march of time
And they can't seem to find the thing on their mind.

They get tired and weary and give up lookin'
And return to their own usual method of cookin'.

So just think as you're eating your egg today –
For the lack of a system – it might be soufflé!

Author: Unknown

George HOUSE

HERITAGE BED & BREAKFAST

STARTERS

Artichoke Appetizer Dip

Did you know? In 1613, Henry Crout sailed Dildo Arm.

1 1/2	cups	marinated artichoke hearts
2	Tbsp	canned green chilies, diced
1/4	cup	mayonnaise
1	cup	cheddar cheese, grated

Procedure

In a bowl, drain the artichokes, reserving the liquid and chop artichokes coarsely. In a 2-cup slow cooker, combine artichokes, chilies, mayonnaise, and cheese. Cover and heat until cheese is melted (45 minutes – or depending on your slow cooker). Stir and mix ingredients, then blend in 1 tablespoon of the reserved artichoke marinade. Serve hot with nacho chips, pita chips or this is excellent spread on crostinis.

Recipe Tips

For cleaning smelly hands after chopping onions or garlic, just rub them on a stainless steel spoon. The steel is supposed to absorb the odour.

Black Bean Dip

Did you know? The town of Dildo was founded in the late 1700s.

2	cups	canned black beans, drained and rinsed
1	small	onion, coarsely chopped
1	small	bell pepper, coarsely chopped
1		garlic clove, chopped
1	Tbsp	red wine vinegar
1	Tbsp	olive oil
1/2	tsp	sugar
		black pepper, freshly ground, to taste

Procedure

Combine all ingredients in a food processor or blender. Blend until the beans are coarsely mashed. This recipe yields 8 servings. This is great as an appetizer served with tortilla chips, pita chips, or nacho chips.

Recipe Tips

If you happen to over-salt a pot of soup, just drop in a peeled potato. The potato will absorb the excess salt.

Crab Dip

***Did you know?** The German flying boat Do-X landed in Dildo Harbour in 1932. At the time it was the largest plane in the world.*

1	cup	cream cheese, softened
1	dash	Tabasco sauce
1/2	cup	butter (no substitutes)
1/2	tsp	garlic powder
1	lb	crab meat (real not imitation crab)
1/4	tsp	white pepper
1		small onion, finely chopped

Procedure

In a pot over low heat melt the cream cheese and butter until all melted. Add the seasonings and crab meat and stir well and heat to warm. This is ideal served over pita chips or can be put in a pastry or tart shell and baked. You can use fresh or canned crab but do not substitute imitation crab.

Recipe Tips

When boiling eggs, add a pinch of salt to keep the shells from cracking.

Creamy Chive Dip

***Did you know?** Richard Gosse and Reuben Reid found a 30-foot-long giant squid in Dildo in 1933.*

2	cups	cottage cheese
1/2	cup	sour cream
4	tsp	garlic powder
4	tsp	onion powder
3	Tbsp	fresh chives, chopped

Procedure

In a bowl mix all ingredients by hand until smooth and then place in the fridge for a few hours. Serve chilled.

Recipe Tips

To clean cast iron cookwear, don't use detergents. Just scrub them with salt and a clean, dry paper towel.

Crab-Stuffed Mushrooms

Todd remembers, "While this is not Ms. Baetzel's personal recipe, it brings back fond memories of the first time I ate at her house and she served crab-stuffed mushrooms. Ms. Baetzel is a favourite returning guest to the B&B."

3/4	lb	medium to large mushrooms
8	Tbsp	butter (no substitutes), melted
6	Tbsp	soft bread crumbs
2	Tbsp	chives, chopped
1/8	tsp	white pepper
2		eggs, slightly beaten
1/2	lb	crab meat from Newfoundland
2	Tbsp	onion, finely chopped
2	Tbsp	mayonnaise
1	tsp	lemon juice

Procedure

Preheat your oven to 375°. Clean your mushrooms with a mushroom brush and remove the mushroom stems from the mushroom caps. Finely chop the mushroom stems.

Brush the mushroom caps with the melted butter and then put them on a sprayed cookie sheet.

In a bowl add the chopped mushroom stems, 5 tablespoons of bread crumbs, chives, white pepper, eggs, crab meat, chopped onion, mayonnaise, and lemon juice. Mix well and then spoon the mixture into the mushroom caps filling each cap.

Now take the reserved bread crumbs and 1 tablespoon of melted butter and mix well and then sprinkle over the tops of the stuffed mushrooms. Bake in a 375° oven for 15 minutes and serve hot or warm.

Recipe Tips

You can add a little bit of finely grated Parmesan cheese to the mixture or even sprinkle a little over the tops of the mushroom caps just before you pop them into the oven. Delicious. This recipe can be used as an appetizer or you can use this as a main vegetarian dish or side dish.

Devilish Eggs

Dale recalls, "Believe it or not, devilled eggs – or as I called them as a kid, devilish eggs – are one of my favourite things to have at a party. They are always the first thing eaten in any buffet and, while they are simplistic to make, they never go out of style."

6		hard-boiled eggs
1/2	tsp	salt
1/4	tsp	pepper
1/2	tsp	mustard
3	Tbsp	mayonnaise
1/2	tsp	vinegar
1/4	tsp	paprika for garnish (optional)

Procedure

Shell the boiled eggs and rinse under cold water to ensure all egg shell is removed. Pat the eggs dry with paper towel. Cut each egg in half lengthwise and scoop the egg yolk in a bowl.

Mash the egg yolks with a fork and add the salt, pepper, mustard, mayonnaise and vinegar and stir well.

Using a piping bag, fill the bag with the mixture and then pipe the mixture back into the egg whites, filling each of the holes, ensuring to pipe a heaping amount. Dust with paprika and serve chilled.

Recipe Tips

We've done a ton of variations to this recipe and you can too, simply by adding some curry powder or garlic powder or even a small amount of horseradish sauce for a peppy version.

Holy Moly Guacamole

Did you know? The first church in Dildo was built in 1878. It held 250 people but did not have a steeple.

6		ripe avocados
6	Tbsp	fresh cilantro, chopped
1		medium red onion, finely diced
4		jalapeño chilies, stemmed, seeded and finely diced
3	Tbsp	lime juice, freshly squeezed
1 1/2	tsp	salt
1/2	tsp	black pepper, freshly ground

Procedure

In a mixing bowl place peeled, quartered and seeded avocados. Mash with a potato masher or fork until chunky. Add the remaining ingredients and combine with a fork. Chill and then serve. Ideal with nacho chips and goes great on a sandwich.

Recipe Tips

Use a sharp knife and slice across the top of the pepper, as if you are removing the stem. However, only cut halfway across, leave the stem intact. Slice lengthwise down one side of the pepper, being sure to leave the pepper intact. Open the jalapeño pepper and hollow it out, removing the seeds with the tip of a sharp knife. Wear plastic gloves to protect your hands from the hot jalapeño peppers. Raw, fresh jalapeño peppers are much hotter than cooked jalapeño peppers and can burn the skin.

Mushroom, Bacon and Onion Tart

Did you know? In 2001, Dildo won the Harrowsmith Magazine award as one of the ten prettiest small towns in Canada.

1		pie crust, frozen or freshly made
6		bacon strips
2 1/2	cups	mushrooms, sliced
1	cup	onion, sliced
2	cups	sour cream
3/4	tsp	salt
3/4	tsp	oregano leaves, dried and crushed
1/8	tsp	black pepper, ground
4		eggs

Procedure

Preheat oven to 425°. Bake your pie crust just until golden, 5-7 minutes then set on rack and cool slightly. Set aside. In a frying pan over medium heat, cook bacon until crisp, about 5 minutes.

Place the bacon on paper towels to remove any excess fat. Crumble the bacon and set aside. Pour off bacon drippings from pan. Add mushrooms and onions and cook, stirring frequently, until any liquid in the pan disappears – approximately 6-8 minutes of cooking time. Allow the mixture to cool.

In a large bowl beat sour cream, eggs, salt, oregano, and black pepper until smooth. Pour over your baked pie crust and top with the cooled mushroom mixture and sprinkle the bacon.

Bake for 15 minutes. Reduce heat to 300°; bake until a knife inserted in the centre comes out clean, 5-7 minutes longer.

Recipe Tips

This is an ideal dish to serve for breakfast, as a dinner main course along with a garden salad or in this case as an appetizer.

Trinity Bay Salt Cod Dip

Did you know? Guglielmo Marconi received the first ever transatlantic wireless transmission on Signal Hill.

2	cups	salt cod
1	cup	extra virgin olive oil
4	cloves	garlic, crushed
1	cup	whipping cream

Procedure

Soak the salt cold in a bowl of cold water for 24 hours changing the water every few hours.

Drain the fish, cut into small pieces, place in shallow pan and add enough water to cover. Heat the water until it reaches a simmer and poach the fish for 8 minutes.

Drain the fish, remove any skin and bones. Combine extra virgin olive oil and crushed garlic in the pan on light heat. In separate pan heat whipping cream just until it reaches a simmer. Add cod to food processor and pulse, then add 1/3 of the olive oil and whipping cream and pulse. Repeat again and again until all oil and cream are gone.

Dip should have the consistency of mashed potatoes. Season with pepper. Serve in a dip bowl with crusty bread, biscuits, or crackers.

Recipe Tips

Before making popcorn on the stove or in an air popper, soak the kernels in water for 10 minutes. Drain the water, then pop as normal. The additional moisture helps the popcorn pop up quicker and fluffier with fewer "old maids."

Spinach Dip

Did you know? "Dildo" is also the traditional name of the two round pegs in a dory that are used to brace oars during rowing.

1 1/2	cups	frozen spinach (usually a 10 oz package)
1	cup	mayonnaise
1/2	cup	can water chestnuts, drained and chopped
1	cup	sour cream
1		package dried vegetable soup mix

Procedure

Mix all ingredients in a bowl and chill in the fridge until ready to serve. This will last for up to 2 days in the fridge.

Recipe Tips

To clean an electric kettle with calcium buildup on the heating element, boil a mixture of half white vinegar and half water, then empty.

George HOUSE

HERITAGE BED & BREAKFAST

BREAKFASTS & SNACKS

Baked Hearty Breakfast

Did you know? Newfoundland was the first place to respond to the Titanic distress signal.

1 1/2	lbs	sausage meat
3/4	cup	onions, chopped
1		dozen eggs (yes, a dozen)
1	cup	cheddar cheese, grated
1	cup	canned mushrooms (must be canned)
1	cup	whipping cream

Procedure

In a frying pan brown the loose sausage meat and onion and remove from pan. Butter or spray an ovenproof dish. Add sausage meat and onion mixture to dish. In the dish, add the eggs and ensure the yolks are broken – use a fork to do this. Add salt and pepper to taste. Sprinkle in 1/2 of the cheese. Pour cream over the top and then sprinkle the mushrooms and add the remaining cheese. Place in fridge overnight and bake in a 350° oven for 40 minutes the following morning.

Blueberry Cheese Pancakes

Did you know? Newfoundland was the first to vaccinate for smallpox.

1 1/2	cups	cottage cheese
4		eggs
1/2	cup	flour
1/4	cup	sugar
2	Tbsp	butter, melted
2	tsp	vanilla
1	cup	blueberries

Procedure

Combine cottage cheese, eggs, flour, sugar and butter in a bowl; mix well. Stir in vanilla; add the blueberries. Cook batter on a hot greased griddle until light brown on both sides; turning once. Serve with room temperature butter and real Canadian maple syrup.

Recipe Tips

Pancakes are lighter and fluffier when you substitute club soda for milk in the batter. Less calories too.

Country Apple Pancakes

Did you know? Newfoundland was the first to have wireless communication in the world.

2	Granny Smith apples, peeled, cored and thinly sliced	
1/2	cup	sugar
2	tsp	cinnamon
1	cup	milk
4		eggs
1	cup	flour
		pinch salt
1/4	cup	butter, unsalted
1/2	cup	brown sugar (packed)

Procedure

Heat oven to 425°. Lightly oil a 10" cast iron skillet. Toss apples with both sugars and cinnamon in a large bowl. Mix milk and eggs in a blender or food processor; add flour and salt and mix to combine. Melt butter in prepared skillet over medium heat. Add apple mixture; cook, stirring often, until sugar melts, about 5 minutes. Remove from heat and pour batter over. Bake until pancake is puffed and golden, 20-30 minutes. Serve at once.

Recipe Tips

This is a great way to start the day and can be accompanied with crispy bacon, whipped butter and of course real Nova Scotia or New Brunswick maple syrup.

Dominion Crepes

Did you know? Newfoundland was the first place to discover proof of the Continental Drift theory.

2		eggs
2		egg yolks
1	tsp	salt
1	cup	flour
1	cup	Dominion Ale or any ale that you have on hand
2	Tbsp	butter, melted, or oil

Procedure

Mix liquids first including melted butter or oil. Incorporate the eggs and then add the flour last. If whisking or blending by hand then mix for 3 minutes until smooth. If making in blender or food processor mix for 1 minute on high speed. Scrape down the sides of the bowl to make sure everything is well whisked. Blend smooth, 30 seconds to 1 minute. Use batter immediately if made in processor or blender, let rest for 1 hour if hand-mixed. Use within 24 hours.

Recipe Tips

These are great savoury crepes for dinner, or you can fill them with just about anything and serve them as an appetizer.

Easy Basic Crepes

Did you know? Newfoundland has the oldest city in North America, St. John's.

3		eggs
1 1/2	cups	flour
1	tsp	sugar
	dash	salt
1 1/2	cups	milk
2	Tbsp	butter, melted, or oil

Procedure

Mix wet ingredients first in the bowl including the melted butter or oil and then add eggs. Add the flour last to the bowl and mix well.

If whisking or blending by hand, mix for 3 minutes until smooth. If making in blender or food processor mix for 1 minute on high speed.

Stop and scrape down the sides. Stir for another minute until mixture is silky smooth and use batter right away for optimum results. You don't need a fancy crepe pan to make these – any non-stick pan will do. You can spray the pan and put just enough batter to cover the bottom. Let it cook through and then turn over and quickly remove from the pan. The best way to serve crepes for a crowd is to preheat your oven to 200° and keep them warm until ready to serve. Remember that the filling will be hot or cold so the temperature of the crepes is not so important.

Blueberry Granola Bars

Did you know? Newfoundland was the first to host a transatlantic flight.

1/2	cup	honey
1/4	cup	brown sugar (packed)
3	Tbsp	vegetable oil
1 1/2	tsp	cinnamon, ground
1 1/2	cups	quick-cooking oats
2	cups	fresh blueberries

Procedure

Preheat oven to 350°. Lightly grease a 9"x9" square baking pan. In a medium saucepan, combine honey, brown sugar, oil and cinnamon.

Bring to a boil, and boil for 2 minutes; do not stir. In a large mixing bowl, combine oats and blueberries. Stir in honey mixture until thoroughly blended. Spread into prepared pan, gently pressing mixture flat.

Bake until lightly browned, about 40 minutes. Cool completely in the pan or on a wire rack. Cut into bars.

Heavenly Baked French Toast

Did you know? Newfoundland hosts the oldest annual sporting event in the world, the Royal Regatta in St. John's.

4		eggs
1	cup	whipping cream
2	thick slices bread, with crusts cut off and cut in 2 pieces	
		powdered sugar
		maple syrup
		vegetable oil
		add pinch of salt

Procedure

Beat eggs, cream, and a pinch of salt and stir vigorously to make a creamy batter. Heat a frying pan with a little bit of vegetable oil.

Dip the bread into the batter and let it soak. Remove the bread and fry in the frying pan until brown on one side, then turn over and brown again on other side. Transfer the browned pieces to a baking sheet and bake at 325° for about 5 minutes or until bread begins to look puffed-up.

Remove from oven and baking sheet and plate with a sprinkling of powdered sugar and serve with warm maple syrup.

Recipe Tips

No "curly" bacon for breakfast when you dip it into cold water before frying.

Honey Granola

Did you know? Newfoundland hosts the most pubs per square foot in Canada.

4	cups	old-fashioned rolled oats
2	cups	nuts, coarsely chopped
1	cup	raisins
3/4	cup	honey
1/2	cup	butter (no substitutes)
2	tsp	cinnamon, ground
1	tsp	vanilla
	dash	salt

Procedure

Combine oats, nuts and raisins in a large bowl; mix well and set aside. Combine honey, butter, cinnamon, vanilla and salt in a saucepan; bring to a boil over high heat and boil 1 minute. Pour honey mixture over oat mixture; toss until well blended. Spread on a lightly greased cookie sheet – don't pat this down. Bake at 350° 20 minutes or until lightly browned; stir every 5 minutes. Cool. Crumble and store at room temperature in airtight container up to 2 weeks.

Recipe Tips

Keep popcorn fresh and encourage more kernels to pop by storing in the freezer.

Morning Riser Apple Pancakes

Did you know? Newfoundland is the only province to have its own encyclopedia, dictionary, pony, and dogs.

1/2	cup	Carnation milk
1/3	cup	biscuit mix
2	Tbsp	sugar, divided
3		eggs, separated
2	Tbsp	orange juice
1/4	tsp	cinnamon, ground
1	medium	apple, cored, quartered, and cut into thin slices
1	Tbsp	75/25 of sugar and cinnamon

Procedure

Preheat oven to 375°. Spray 10" ovenproof skillet. Place in oven for 10 minutes. Place evaporated milk, baking mix, 1 tablespoon sugar, egg yolks, orange juice and cinnamon in blender; blend until smooth. Beat egg whites in large mixing bowl until soft peaks form; gradually add remaining sugar. Beat until stiff peaks form. Fold milk mixture into egg whites. Pour batter into hot skillet. Gently push each apple slice about 1/2" into batter, peel side up, to form a spoke-like pattern around batter. Sprinkle with cinnamon-sugar. Bake for 10-15 minutes or until set. Serve immediately.

Recipe Tips

Before opening a package of bacon, roll it. This helps separate the slices for easy removal of individual slices.

Mushroom Egg Divan

Did you know? Dorset Eskimo artifacts were found on Dildo Island in 1995, dated between AD 150 and AD 750.

5 1/2	cups	fresh mushrooms, sliced
1	can	cream of mushroom soup (condensed)
2	Tbsp	chives, chopped
1	cup	cheddar cheese, grated
2		packages of frozen broccoli spears
6		eggs, hard-cooked, peeled and halved
4	Tbsp	butter
1/4	cup	milk
1/8	tsp	pepper

Procedure

Preheat oven to 375°.

In a large skillet melt butter. Add mushrooms; sauté until golden, about 5 minutes. Stir in soup, milk, chives and black pepper. Bring to the boiling point. Stir in half the cheese; cook and stir until cheese melts.

Put broccoli in a buttered 9"x9" square baking pan. Top with eggs. Pour sauce over all. Sprinkle with remaining cheese. Bake uncovered, until hot and bubbly, about 15 minutes.

Mushroom & Spinach Omelette

Did you know? Dildo Island was named before 1711.

1 1/2	cups	mushrooms, sliced
3	Tbsp	butter
2	Tbsp	onion, minced
4		eggs
1	Tbsp	Parmesan cheese, grated
1/4	tsp	salt
1/4	tsp	oregano leaves, dried and crushed
1/8	tsp	pepper
1/2	cup	spinach, cooked and chopped

Procedure

Rinse, pat dry and slice mushrooms; set aside. In a medium pan melt 1 tablespoon of butter. Add mushrooms and onion; sauté until golden, about 5 minutes; remove from skillet. In a mixing bowl combine eggs, salt, oregano and pepper.

In the skillet used to sauté mushrooms, melt remaining 2 tablespoons of butter. Pour in egg mixture. Cook over moderate heat letting uncooked egg run under the cooked portion.

When almost set, top with mushroom mixture and spinach. Sprinkle with Parmesan cheese. Place skillet under a preheated, moderately hot broiler until top of omelette is set. Turn out onto a plate and serve.

Portobello Quiche

Did you know? John Guy noted in his journal dated 1612 that there was evidence of a Beothuk Indian camp on Dildo Island.

3	cups	mushrooms, sliced (button and portobello work best)
4	Tbsp	butter (no substitutes)
3/4	cup	onion, finely chopped
4		eggs, slightly beaten
1		pie shell
2	cups	heavy cream
1/4	tsp	nutmeg
		salt and pepper, and cayenne pepper to taste

Procedure

Chop the mushrooms until they are very fine in consistency and mixed well. In a pan add the mushrooms and 2 tablespoons of butter and cook, stirring until all mushrooms are softened. Cover and simmer the pan for 30 minutes and then remove from heat and let the mixture cool.

Preheat your oven to 450° and bake a pie shell for 5 minutes.

In the pan melt the remaining butter and add the onions and cook until softened. In a bowl combine the eggs, cream, nutmeg, cayenne, salt and pepper and stir. Add the mushrooms and onions and mix well.

Pour into the baked pie shell and return to oven and bake for an additional 15 minutes at 450° and then reduce the heat to 350° and bake for an additional 15 minutes. Use a knife to test the middle of the quiche to see that it removes clean.

Quiche Lorraine

Did you know? Newfoundland's first cod fish hatchery was constructed on Dildo Island in 1889, just after the George House was built.

1		9″ deep-dish pie shell, unbaked
6		slices bacon, chopped
1/2	cup	onion, finely chopped
1 1/2	cups	Swiss cheese, grated
1	can	Carnation milk
3		eggs, well-beaten
1/4	tsp	salt
1/8	tsp	pepper
1/8	tsp	nutmeg, ground

Procedure

Preheat oven to 350°.

Cook bacon in large skillet over medium heat. When bacon starts to turn brown, add onion. Cook until bacon is crisp; drain. Sprinkle cheese into bottom of pie shell. Top with bacon mixture.

Combine evaporated milk, eggs, salt, pepper and nutmeg in small bowl until blended. Pour into pie shell.

Bake for 30-35 minutes or until knife inserted halfway between centre and edge comes out clean. Cool for 5 minutes on wire rack before serving.

Rock Granola

Did you know? The cod fish hatchery on Dildo Island was once the largest in the world.

4	cups	rolled oats
1/4	cup	safflower oil
1/4	cup	honey
1 1/2	tsp	vanilla
1/2	cup	sesame seeds
1/2	cup	almonds, chopped and unsalted
1/2	cup	cashews, chopped and unsalted
1	cup	raisins

Procedure

Preheat your oven to 350°. Pour the rolled oats over a large cookie sheet and toast in the oven for 15 minutes, stirring every 5 minutes to ensure they don't burn.

In a pot combine oil, honey and vanilla. Heat until warm and then set aside. In a large bowl combine the sesame seeds, almonds and cashews. Pour the warm honey and oil mixture over the seeds and nuts. Stir to combine and then pour the mixture over the oats and blend well.

Bake for 20 minutes, ensuring to turn oats over every 5 minutes. Be careful to ensure the mixture doesn't burn. Add the raisins at the end when the mixture is removed from the oven.

Recipe Tips

There are a ton of granola recipes but you can change this one by adding dried coconut, dried fruits, Craisins, or other nuts.

Salmon Quiche

Did you know? The history of Dildo and area goes back as far as 2000 BC.

8		eggs
1 1/2	cups	milk
1/2	cup	flour
1 1/2	tsp	baking powder
2	cups	salmon, flaked and cooked, or canned, drained
1 1/2	cups	cheddar cheese, grated
2		green onion, chopped
1/2	cup	butter, melted
		salt and pepper to taste

Procedure

Preheat the oven to 350°. In a large bowl beat the eggs and milk together. Add the white flour and baking powder and mix well. Stir in the salmon, cheese, green onions, butter, salt and pepper.

Pour the mixture into a sprayed 10" quiche pan and bake for 45-50 minutes. Let stand for 10 minutes before serving.

Scrambled Eggs 365

We call this recipe scrambled egg 365 as this is a staple that is served at the bed and breakfast almost every day we are open.

6		eggs, slightly beaten
1/2	tsp	salt
1/2	tsp	pepper
6	Tbsp	cream
3	Tbsp	butter (no substitutes)

Procedure

In a bowl combine the eggs, salt, pepper, milk and butter. Cook in a sprayed or non-stick pan over medium heat stirring constantly until almost set. Let cook without stirring the final minute or two and then plate and serve.

Tomato & Basil Breakfast Quiche

On mornings when we serve quiche we make it in advance and keep it in a warm oven to serve. For a complete breakfast simply add some pan potatoes and fresh fruit. They'll love you for it.

1		9″ deep-dish pie shell, unbaked
1 1/2	cups	sour cream
1/2	cup	Carnation milk
1/2	cup	Parmesan cheese, grated
4		eggs, lightly beaten
1/4	tsp	salt
1/4	tsp	pepper
3	Tbsp	dry bread crumbs
1	tsp	dried basil leaves
3		cloves garlic, finely chopped
1 3/4	cups	fresh or canned tomatoes, diced and drained well!
1/4	cup	ripe olives, chopped (optional)

Procedure

Preheat oven to 350°.

Whisk sour cream, evaporated milk, 1/4 cup cheese, eggs, salt and pepper in medium bowl; pour into pie shell. Combine remaining cheese, bread crumbs, basil and garlic in small bowl; sprinkle over sour cream mixture. Top with tomatoes and olives.

Bake for 50-60 minutes or until knife inserted near centre comes out clean. Cool on wire rack for 5 minutes before serving.

Recipe Tips

You can blind bake the pie shell for 10 minutes prior to pouring in the quiche mixture.

Stuffed French Toast With Blueberries

Did you know? Maritime Archaic Indians once resided in Anderson's Cove.

French Toast

6		eggs
1	tsp	orange peel, grated
2/3	cup	orange juice
3	Tbsp	sugar, divided
		pinch salt
1	cup	fresh or frozen blueberries (thawed and drained, if frozen)
8		slices of bread, homemade, unsliced, and make 2″ slices
1/3	cup	almonds, sliced

Procedure

Preheat oven to 400°. Spray a large baking sheet with cooking spray.

In a medium bowl beat eggs, peel, juice, 2 tablespoons of the sugar and the salt until well blended. Pour into a 13"x9"x2" baking pan; set aside.

In a small bowl combine blueberries and the remaining 1 tablespoon sugar; set aside. With the tip of a sharp knife, cut a 1 1/2" wide pocket in the side of each bread slice. Fill pockets with reserved blueberry mixture, dividing evenly. Place filled slices in egg mixture. Let stand, turning once, until egg mixture is absorbed, about 5 minutes on each side. Arrange bread on prepared baking sheet; sprinkle with almonds. Bake until golden brown, about 15 minutes, turning slices after 10 minutes. Serve with Blueberry Orange Sauce.

Blueberry Orange Sauce

3	Tbsp	sugar
1	Tbsp	cornstarch
1/8	tsp	salt
1/4	cup	orange juice
1	cup	fresh or frozen blueberries
1	cup	orange sections (about 2 oranges)

In a cup combine sugar, cornstarch, and salt; set aside. In a small saucepan bring orange juice and 1/4 cup water to a boil. Add blueberries and orange sections. Return to a boil; cook until liquid is released from fruit, about 2 minutes. Stir in sugar mixture; cook, stirring constantly, until sauce thickens, 1-2 minutes.

Waffle Mix

Waffle irons are really inexpensive these days and waffles are making a comeback for breakfast. Pick yourself up a waffle iron and try this recipe – you'll have light and fluffy waffles and impress everyone at the breakfast table. We love the waffle irons that you pour in the batter and then invert the iron so it bakes evenly on both sides. They are also an easy way to make dessert by adding a scoop of ice cream, shake icing sugar and some strawberries over them.

1 1/2	cups	flour
3	tsp	baking powder
1/2	tsp	salt
1	Tbsp	sugar
1	cup	milk
2		eggs, separated
3	Tbsp	butter, melted

Procedure

In a bowl sift the flour with the baking powder, salt and sugar. Make a well in the centre and add the milk, egg yolks, and melted butter. Whisk all the ingredients together. There will be lumps – don't fret.

Beat the egg whites in another bowl until stiff and then fold them into the batter.

Pour batter into waffle iron and use directions of your waffle iron to bake.

BREADS, BISCUITS & MUFFINS

Blueberry Scones

Did you know? Newfoundland is the most easterly point in North America.

2	cups	flour
3	Tbsp	sugar, plus a bit more for tops
1	Tbsp	baking powder
3/4	tsp	salt
6	Tbsp	butter, cold and unsalted, cut into pieces
1 1/2	cups	fresh blueberries, picked over and rinsed
1	tsp	lemon zest, grated
1/3	cup	heavy cream, plus more for brushing tops
2		eggs, lightly beaten

Procedure

Adjust rack to centre of oven, and heat to 400°. Place a Silpat rubber pad on a baking sheet, and set aside.

In a large bowl, sift together flour, 3 tablespoons sugar, baking powder, and salt. Using a pastry blender, or two knives, cut in butter until the largest pieces are the size of small peas. Stir in blueberries and zest.

Using a fork, whisk together the cream and the eggs in a bowl. Make a well in the centre of dry ingredients, and pour in cream mixture. Stir lightly with fork just until dough comes together. Turn out onto a lightly floured surface, and knead a few times to mix well.

Pat dough into about 1 1/4" thick and cut into serving pieces. Transfer to prepared baking sheet. Brush tops with cream, and sprinkle with sugar. Bake until golden brown, 20-22 minutes. Transfer scones from baking sheet to wire racks to cool.

Captain Dildo's Cheese Scones

Did you know? The Newfoundland dog has webbed feet.

2	cups	flour
2 1/2	tsp	baking powder
1/2	tsp	mustard powder
1/2	tsp	salt
1/2	cup	cold butter, chopped
3/4	cup	cheddar cheese, grated (old tastes best)
2/3	cup	milk
1		egg, beaten

Procedure

Preheat your oven to 450°. In a large bowl sift together the flour, baking powder, mustard powder and salt. Add the butter and using your hands rub the butter into the flour mixture until it resembles a crumbly mixture. Stir in 1/2 cup of the grated cheddar into the mixture. Make a hole in the centre of the mixture and add the milk and beaten egg. Stir using a wooden spoon until it creates a soft sticky dough. Turn the dough out onto a floured countertop and roll out the dough and cut into triangles. Put the triangles on a cookie sheet and lightly brush them with milk and then top with the remaining cheddar cheese. Let rest for 20 minutes on the cookie sheet prior to putting them in the oven.

Bake for 15 minutes.

Country-Style Ham Biscuits

1	cup	flour
2	tsp	baking powder
1/8	tsp	salt
1/4	tsp	dry mustard
3	Tbsp	shortening
1	cup	roasted ham, cooked and minced
1/2	cup	milk

Procedure

Preheat the oven to 450° and in a bowl combine flour, salt, mustard and baking powder. Using your fingertips mix well with the shortening. Add the minced cooked ham and slowly add the milk to create a soft dough mixture. Knead the dough mixture on a floured countertop for 1 minute. Roll out to 1/2" thickness and cut into biscuit rounds.

Bake in the oven for 10 minutes until done. Oh yum!

Fisherman's Cheese Biscuits

2	cups	flour
4	tsp	baking powder
2	Tbsp	sugar
3/4	tsp	salt
1	cup	cheddar cheese, grated (old tastes best)
1/3	cup	vegetable oil
3/4	cup	milk

Procedure

Preheat your oven to 425°. In a large bowl mix together flour, baking powder, sugar and salt. Add the grated cheddar cheese and incorporate well. Add the vegetable oil and milk and mix well. This should turn the mixture into a soft dough ball. If too dry to create a dough ball add a very little amount of extra milk.

Lightly flour a countertop and turn out the dough. Knead the dough for 1 minute and then roll out the dough into 3/4" and use a cookie or biscuit cutter and cut out biscuits. Place on a sprayed cookie sheet and bake in a 425° oven for 15 minutes or until lightly golden brown.

Mary Walker's Traditional Tea Biscuits

We emailed a very special lady, Mary Walker, and asked her if she would like to contribute a recipe to our book. She didn't hesitate and we are proud that she has offered us her tried, tested and true recipe for traditional tea biscuits. We've made several batches of these biscuits and they are excellent served hot or warm with real butter and homemade jams, or even room temperature the following day with a piece of real cheddar cheese and a hot cup of tea. I met Mary a few years ago through an introduction by her daughter. Mary has a real bright spirit and it is our pleasure to include her recipe. Mary and her partner Bud spend their time between Dartmouth, Nova Scotia, and Oromocto, New Brunswick.

3	cups	flour
1 1/2	tsp	baking soda
3	tsp	cream of tartar
1	tsp	baking powder
1	tsp	salt
1/3	cup	shortening
1 1/2	cups	milk

Procedure

Preheat your oven to 450°. In a large bowl mix the dry ingredients and cut in the shortening and then mix in the milk. The dough will be wet in texture.

Turn the dough onto a floured surface and knead until you are able to pat out the dough to 3/4" thick. Cut out the individual biscuits with a floured cookie cutter or water glass, and place the biscuits on a cookie sheet.

Bake in a 450° oven for approximately 10 minutes.

Louisdale Tea Biscuits

Dale remembers, "I've made many a trip to Louisdale in Cape Breton, Nova Scotia, to visit the Sampson Family. Tommy, Beatrice, Greg, Diane, Brad, Melanie, Dale, and Tanya Sampson are all such wonderful people and great home-cooked food is a key component in their daily lives. Beatrice is a wonderful baker and her son Dale is considered by us to be a Barbecue Grill Master. Louisdale is an amazing place and the Sampson family are truly special to me! This recipe is named in honour of them, and if you ever have a chance to visit the area, please do!"

4	cups	flour
8	tsp	baking powder
1	tsp	salt
2	Tbsp	sugar
3/4	cup	shortening
1		egg
2	cups	milk

Procedure

Mix flour, baking powder, salt and sugar together. Add shortening and mix using pastry blender. Add lightly beaten egg and 2 cups of milk to the mixture. Knead dough on a floured countertop for 1 minute. Roll out and cut into circles. Bake at 425° for 15-20 minutes. Serve warm or cold.

Mushroom Biscuits

Did you know? Newfoundland boasts 17,000 kms of rugged coastline.

3	cups	mushrooms
2	Tbsp	butter
1/4	cup	onion, finely chopped
1/4	tsp	thyme, ground
1/8	tsp	white pepper
2	cups	biscuit mix
2/3	cup	milk

Procedure

Rinse, pat dry and coarsely chop mushrooms to make 3 cups. In a medium skillet, heat butter. Add mushrooms and onion; sauté until lightly browned about 5 minutes, stirring occasionally. Sprinkle with thyme and white pepper. Cool slightly.

Blend mushroom mixture into biscuit mix. Add milk and stir until well-mixed. Drop by the tablespoonful onto greased cookie sheets 2" apart. Bake in a preheated oven (450°) 12 minutes or until nicely browned.

Recipe Tips

Always store mushrooms in paper bags!

Oh So Sweet Tea Buns

Did you know? Newfoundland is home to North America's most spectacular seabird sanctuary, Cape St. Mary's – a must-see attraction and only 90 minutes from Dildo.

3	cups	flour
1/2	cup	coconut
2	Tbsp	custard powder
1	cup	milk
1/2	cup	sugar
5	tsp	baking powder
3/4	cup	butter
1/2	tsp	salt
2		eggs

Procedure

Preheat your oven to 375°. In a bowl mix all the dry ingredients together. Cut in the butter with a pastry blender until mixture resembles a crumbly blend. Mix the eggs and milk together in a bowl and then add to the flour mixture to create a soft biscuit dough.

Roll out the dough on a floured counter and cut with a 1" cookie cutter. Bake on a sprayed cookie sheet in a 375° oven for 15-20 minutes or golden on top.

1864 Potato Bread

In 1864 there was a potato famine in New Brunswick, Nova Scotia, and of course Newfoundland. While the potato famine came from Ireland and caused many deaths, mass starvation, and disease, many immigrated to Newfoundland to escape it. This recipe would not have been popular back then as it is today.

1	small	potato, shredded
1/2	cup	orange juice concentrate
1/4	cup	water
1/3	cup	orange marmalade
1/4	cup	vegetable oil
1		egg, beaten
3	cups	flour
1/2	cup	sugar
2	tsp	baking powder
1/4	tsp	salt

Procedure

Cook the shredded potato in just enough water to cover it, for 10 min. Cool and drain.

Combine cooled and drained potato with orange juice concentrate, water, marmalade, oil and egg.

In a large bowl, sift together the flour, sugar, baking powder and salt. Add the liquid ingredients and stir just until combined.

Spoon batter into 3 greased mini loaf pans and bake at 350° for 30-35 minutes or until tester comes out clean. Cool in pans for 10 min. then remove from pan and let cool.

Banana Bread

1	cup	sugar
4	Tbsp	butter, softened
2		eggs
3		bananas, mashed
1/2	cup	walnuts
1	tsp	baking soda
2	cups	flour
1	tsp	salt

Procedure

Preheat your oven to 350°. In a large bowl cream the butter and then add the sugar and eggs and mix well. Add the bananas, baking soda, flour and salt and mix well.

Bake in a loaf pan for 1 hour or until done with the toothpick test.

Recipe Tips

You can add chopped walnuts to this recipe – as Dale's mom used to do and it is delicious.

Barrens Cornbread

We love this cornbread and it is best served warm with some soft butter and molasses dripping over it. Great with a cup of tea, served with a hot bowl of chili or soup, or even as a bread to go with the evening's dinner.

1	cup	yellow cornmeal
1	Tbsp	whole wheat flour
1/4	cup	wheat bran, unprocessed and uncooked
1	tsp	baking soda
1	tsp	salt
1	cup	buttermilk
1		egg
3	Tbsp	vegetable oil

Procedure

Preheat the oven to 425°. Combine the dry ingredients in a large bowl. Combine the buttermilk, egg, and oil and add to the dry ingredients, stirring just until the dry ingredients are moistened.

Pour the batter into an 8"x8" pan. Bake for 20 minutes.

Dinner Rolls

While we cannot remember who passed this recipe along to us, it makes wonderful and easy dinner rolls. Try them just once and you'll be hooked.

2		packages dry yeast
3/4	cup	warm water
1/3	cup	sugar
1	tsp	salt
1		egg, slightly beaten
1/2	cup	butter (no substitutes), melted
3 1/2	cups	white flour

Procedure

Preheat your oven to 375°. Dissolve the dry yeast in the warm water. Add sugar, salt, egg, butter, and 1 cup of flour and mix well. Shape the mixture into a dough ball. Grease the dough all over. Return the dough to the bowl, cover it and let it rise until doubled. Punch down the dough and shape into 12 balls. Let the rolls rise for 30 minutes or longer. Bake for 10-12 minutes in a 375° oven. Remove from oven and if you desire brush melted butter over the tops for a golden look.

Recipe Tips

Toothpaste is a great silver cleaner.

It's That Easy Buns

1	cup	margarine
1	tsp	vanilla
1	cup	sugar
1	cup	milk
4	cups	flour
1		egg
4	tsp	baking powder

Procedure

Preheat your oven to 350°. In a bowl mix together all ingredients until well incorporated.

Lightly flour a countertop and turn dough out onto counter. Roll out the dough to 1/2" thick and then use a cookie cutter to cut out biscuit buns. Bake at 350° for 10-12 minutes or until golden brown.

Heart's Content Carrot & Zucchini Bread

On your travels around the Baccalieu Trail make sure to check out Grow Dat Farms in Heart's Content. They grow all kinds of great fruits and vegetables and we are always pleased to cook with their daily fresh pickings. They offer wonderful tours of their farm and welcome guests.

3		eggs
1 3/4	cups	sugar
1	cup	vegetable oil
2	tsp	vanilla
2 1/3	cups	flour
2	tsp	baking soda
1/4	tsp	baking powder
1	tsp	salt
1	tsp	cinnamon
1 1/2	cups	zucchini, grated, with any moisture removed
1 1/2	cups	carrots, grated
1	cup	nuts, chopped
1/2	cup	raisins

Procedure

Preheat your oven to 350°. Spray two 9"x5" loaf pans.

In a large bowl, mix eggs, sugar, oil, and vanilla. Sift in the flour, baking soda, baking powder, salt, and cinnamon and mix very well. Stir in zucchini, carrots, nuts, and raisins.

Divide the batter into the two loaf pans and bake for 60 minutes and use a toothpick to check to ensure that the loaves are well-baked.

Cool for 10 minutes on a wire rack before removing from the loaf pans.

I'se The B'y Gingerbread

Gingerbread has a long history and was first thought to be made by Catholic monks from Europe for holidays and events. Ginger has a great preservative quality and as such was popular with sailors as they headed out over the waves.

1/2	cup	sugar
1/2	cup	butter, softened
1		egg, beaten
1	cup	molasses
2 1/2	cups	flour
1 1/2	tsp	baking soda
1	tsp	cinnamon
1	tsp	ginger
1/2	tsp	cloves, ground
1/2	tsp	salt
1	cup	water, hot

Procedure

Preheat your oven to 350°.

In a bowl mix together the flour, cinnamon, ginger, and cloves. In a separate bowl begin by creaming butter and sugar together, mixing well. Add the beaten egg and molasses to the butter and sugar mixture and mix well. Now add the dry flour mixture into the wet mixture and mix well. Mix the baking soda in the hot water and then add to the batter. Beat everything until smooth.

Bake in a 350° oven for 1 3/4 hours.

Recipe Tips

Before measuring molasses grease the cup for ease of removing the molasses.

Joyce's Partridgeberry-Orange Bread

Todd notes, "We've called this recipe Joyce's Partridgeberry-Orange Bread after Joyce Smith of Dildo as she has happily picked many gallons of partridgeberries over the years. Her berries are always picked clean of leaves and picked when they are perfectly ripe. We don't know how she does it and she'll never tell us where she gets them, but we're just happy to be recipients of nature's bounty."

2	Tbsp	butter, room temperature
1		egg
1	cup	sugar
3/4	cup	orange juice
1/4	tsp	orange extract
2	cups	flour
1	tsp	baking powder
1/2	tsp	baking soda
1/2	tsp	salt
2	cups	whole fresh partridgeberries, or frozen partridgeberries that are thawed
1/2	cup	walnuts, chopped

Procedure

Preheat your oven to 350°. Spray a 9"x5" loaf pan.

In a large bowl combine butter, egg, and sugar and mix well. Add the orange juice and extract. Sift in the flour, baking powder, baking soda and salt. Stir until mixture is wet. Fold in partridgeberries and walnuts.

Pour the batter into a loaf pan and bake for 60 minutes or use a toothpick to check to ensure the cake is well-cooked. Cool the cake on a wire rack for 20 minutes before removing the loaf from the pan.

Recipe Tips

This can also be made with fresh or frozen cranberries, but we suggest you try it with the partridgeberries.

Nana Farrell's Molasses Buns

Dale recalls, "In the 70s my mom and I made many trips on VIA Rail from New Brunswick to Trenton, Nova Scotia, to visit Nana. While she was known for her biscuits, I can recall her making these molasses buns. My mom kept the recipe; I was fortunate to get her recipe cards, and this was in the recipe box. Both Nana Farrell and Mom have passed on but will be remembered with this recipe for years to come."

4	cups	flour
1	cup	raisins
1/8	tsp	salt
1/2	tsp	cinnamon
1	cup	shortening
2	tsp	baking soda
2	cups	molasses
1	tsp	vanilla
1	tsp	baking powder
1/2	tsp	allspice
1/2	cup	butter

Procedure

In a saucepan mix the butter and shortening and melt. Add the molasses and vanilla and mix well. In a measuring cup add the baking soda and add a drizzle of water enough to dissolve the baking soda.

Stir the baking soda mixture into the molasses until it foams. In a separate bowl add the cinnamon, allspice, salt and baking powder into the flour. Add the raisins to the flour mixture. Add the dry mixture into the molasses mixture and mix thoroughly.

If the mixture is too dry add a little bit of water, roll the mixture out and cut with cookie cutter.

Bake in a 350° oven for 15-20 minutes.

Recipe Tips

To banish ants from the kitchen, find out where they are coming in and cover the hole with petroleum jelly.

Onion Beer Bread

3	cups	self-rising flour
1	tsp	sugar
1/2	tsp	salt
1 1/3	cups	room-temperature beer (almost 1 full can)
2		eggs, beaten
3/4	cup	onion, minced

Procedure

Preheat the oven to 350°. Combine all ingredients. Pour into a lightly sprayed 9" loaf pan and bake for 50 minutes until a toothpick comes out clean.

Recipe Tips

Don't use the full can of beer. Save the last few sips for yourself.

Apple Bran Muffins

1	cup	flour
1/3	cup	brown sugar (packed)
2	tsp	baking powder
1/2	tsp	salt
1/2	tsp	cinnamon, ground
1/4	tsp	nutmeg, ground
1	cup	apple, peeled and finely chopped
3/4	cup	water
1/2	cup	powdered milk
1/4	cup	vegetable oil
1		egg
2	cups	bran flakes cereal

Procedure

Preheat oven to 400°. Grease or line 12 muffin cups.

Combine flour, sugar, baking powder, salt, cinnamon and nutmeg in medium bowl. Mix apple, water, dry milk, vegetable oil and egg in small bowl; add to flour mixture and stir until moistened. Stir in cereal. Spoon into prepared muffin cups, filling 2/3 full.

Bake for 12-15 minutes or until wooden pick inserted in centre comes out clean. Remove to wire rack; cool slightly. Serve warm.

Blueberry Muffins

6	Tbsp	butter
3/4	cup	sugar
2		eggs
2	cups	flour
2	tsp	baking powder
1/2	tsp	salt
1/2	cup	milk
2	tsp	vanilla
1 1/2	cups	fresh or frozen blueberries, thawed and drained
1	Tbsp	sugar mixed with 1/2 teaspoon cinnamon

Procedure

Preheat your oven to 375°. Grease 12 muffin cups generously; a vegetable oil pan spray works well.

In a large mixing bowl, cream together the butter and sugar until they're light and fluffy. Add the eggs, one at a time, beating well after each addition.

In a separate bowl, whisk together the flour, baking powder and salt. Add the dry ingredients to the creamed mixture, and beat well. Stir in the milk and vanilla, mixing only until smooth. Gently stir in the berries.

Fill the muffin cups 3/4 to almost full, using all of the batter. Sprinkle with the cinnamon sugar. Bake the muffins for 30 minutes, until they're light golden brown, remove them from the oven, and place the pan on a rack to cool for 10 minutes.

Cranberry Nut Muffins

2	cups	flour
1/2	cup	sugar
1/2	tsp	salt
1	Tbsp	baking powder
1	cup	dried cranberries
1/2	cup	walnuts, chopped
1	cup	milk
1/4	cup	butter (no substitutes)
2		eggs

Procedure

Preheat your oven to 500°.

Blend together the dry ingredients until they are thoroughly mixed. Add the berries and nuts, and stir them until they are evenly coated.

In a separate bowl, beat the liquid ingredients together until they are well mixed.

Pour the wet ingredients into the dry. Take a fork or wire whisk and blend the two for 20 seconds and no more. The secret to light and tender muffins lies in this final blending. It's okay if you've left some lumps that look as if they want more stirring. They really don't. So, no matter how hard it is, resist the impulse.

Fill the cups of a lightly greased, 12-cup muffin tin three-quarters full. As soon as the muffins are in the oven, DROP THE TEMPERATURE TO 400° (this is important). Bake for about 20 minutes or until they're a lovely, golden brown. Remove from pan and cool on a wire rack.

Decadent Muffins

2	cups	flour
1/2	cup	sugar
1/4	cup	brown sugar (packed)
2 1/2	tsp	baking powder
1/2	tsp	salt
3/4	cup	milk
1		egg, slightly beaten
1/4	cup	butter (no substitutes)
1/2	tsp	lemon peel, grated
2	cups	white chocolate chips or wafers
1 1/2	cups	fresh or frozen blueberries
		Streusel Topping (recipe follows)

Procedure

Preheat oven to 375°. Paper line 18 muffin cups.

Combine flour, granulated sugar, brown sugar, baking powder and salt in large bowl. Stir in milk, egg, butter and lemon peel. Stir in 1 1/2 cups white chocolate chips and blueberries. Spoon into prepared muffin cups, filling almost full. Sprinkle with Streusel Topping.

Bake for 22-25 minutes or until wooden pick inserted in centre comes out clean. Cool in pans for 5 minutes; remove to wire racks to cool slightly.

Place remaining white chocolate chips in small, heavy-duty plastic bag. Microwave on MEDIUM-HIGH (70%) power for 30 seconds; knead. Microwave at additional 10- to 20-second intervals, kneading until smooth. Cut tiny corner from bag; squeeze to drizzle over muffins. Serve warm.

Streusel Topping

Combine 1/3 cup granulated sugar, 1/4 cup all-purpose flour, and 1/4 teaspoon ground cinnamon in small bowl. Cut in 3 tablespoons butter or margarine with pastry blender or two knives until mixture resembles coarse crumbs.

Recipe Tips

To make lighter muffins place the greased pans in the oven for a minute or two before adding the muffin mix.

Glory Glory It's Morning Muffins

This is a super recipe to make and freeze. Take out a few at a time, and when they thaw, they taste as fresh as when they were first baked.

4		eggs
1 1/3	cups	vegetable oil
1	tsp	vanilla
3	cups	flour
1 1/4	cups	brown sugar
3	tsp	baking soda
3/4	tsp	salt
3	tsp	cinnamon
3	cups	carrot, shredded
3/4	cup	coconut, flaked or shredded
1		large apple, shredded
1/3	cup	nuts
1/2	cup	raisins

Procedure

Preheat your oven to 350°. In a mixing bowl beat eggs, oil, and vanilla. In a separate bowl combine all remaining ingredients and then stir into egg mixture just until moistened.

Spoon into greased muffin pan and bake for 15-20 minutes.

Harvest Pumpkin Muffins

1/2	cup	butter, unsalted
3/4	cup	canned solid-pack pumpkin
1/4	cup	buttermilk, well-shaken
2		eggs
3	Tbsp	molasses
1	tsp	vanilla
1	cup	flour
1	cup	whole wheat flour
1 1/2	tsp	baking powder
1	tsp	cinnamon, ground
1/2	tsp	ginger, ground
1/4	tsp	cloves, ground
1/8	tsp	nutmeg, freshly grated
1/2	tsp	salt
1/4	tsp	baking soda
3/4	cup	brown sugar (packed)
3/4	cup	pitted dates, chopped (about 4 oz)
3/4	cup	walnuts, finely chopped (about 3 oz)

Procedure

Preheat oven to 400° and grease 12 1/2-cup muffin cups.

Melt butter and cool slightly. In a bowl whisk together butter, pumpkin, buttermilk, eggs, molasses, and vanilla.

Into a large bowl sift together flours, baking powder, spices, salt, and baking soda and whisk in brown sugar. Add pumpkin mixture, stirring just until combined. Stir in dates and divide batter among cups.

Sprinkle walnuts evenly over batter in each cup and bake muffins in middle of oven 20-25 minutes, or until puffed and a tester comes out clean. Cool muffins in cups 5 minutes and turn out onto a rack.

Recipe Tips

General rule of thumb: if your muffin batter has lumps in it, it is perfect.

Healthy Banana Blueberry Muffins

2		large ripe bananas
1/2	cup	banana yogourt
1		egg, lightly beaten
1 1/2	cups	flour
3/4	cup	sugar
1 1/2	tsp	baking soda
1	cup	fresh or frozen blueberries, thawed and drained

Procedure

Preheat your oven to 350° and spray a muffin pan.

In a large bowl combine mashed bananas, yogourt and egg and mix thoroughly. Add the flour, sugar, and baking soda and stir just until all the ingredients are well mixed.

Gently fold in the blueberries so as not to crush them. Spoon the batter into the muffin pans about 3/4 full.

Bake for 30 minutes or until the tops are brown. Remove from the oven and cool on wire rack for 10 minutes before removing from the pan.

Recipe Tips

Always preheat your oven for 10 minutes unless stated otherwise in a recipe.

Buttermilk Rhubarb Muffin

1 1/2	cups	brown sugar
1/4	cup	vegetable oil
1		egg
2	tsp	vanilla
1	cup	buttermilk
1 1/2	cups	rhubarb, finely chopped
2 1/2	cups	flour
1	tsp	baking powder
1	tsp	baking soda
1/2	tsp	salt

Procedure

Preheat your oven to 350 degrees. In a large bowl mix together the oil, egg, vanilla and buttermilk. In a separate bowl mix together brown sugar, flour, baking powder, baking soda and salt.

Add the rhubarb into the wet mixture and then add the dry ingredients to the wet mixture and incorporate well. Pour batter into sprayed muffin tin pan.

Bake in a 350 degree oven for 15-20 minutes.

Inn By The Bay Muffins

1	cup	quick-cooking oats
1	cup	sour milk
1		egg
1/2	cup	brown sugar
1/2	cup	shortening, melted
1	cup	flour
1/2	tsp	salt
1	tsp	baking powder
1/2	tsp	soda

Procedure

To make sour milk, add 1 tablespoon of vinegar to a measuring cup and fill up to the 1-cup level with fresh milk. Let it sit on the counter for 15 minutes and *voila*! You have sour milk.

Soak oatmeal in sour milk 1 hour; add egg and beat well. Add sugar and mix. Add cooled shortening. Add flour sifted with salt, baking powder and soda.

Bake in greased muffin pans in hot oven (400°) 15-20 minutes.

Partridgeberry Muffins

1 1/2	cups	flour
1	cup	whole wheat flour
2	tsp	baking powder
2	tsp	cinnamon
2		eggs, beaten
1/4	cup	sugar
1/2	cup	unsweetened applesauce
2	Tbsp	canola oil
1/4	cup	orange juice
1	tsp	orange extract
1	cup	fresh or frozen partridgeberries

Procedure

Preheat the oven to 350°. Combine the flours, baking powder, and cinnamon in a medium bowl. Set aside.

In a large bowl, combine the remaining ingredients. Add the dry ingredients slowly to the large bowl and mix until blended. Do not over-beat. Pour the batter into 12 non-stick muffin cups and bake for 20-25 minutes. Remove from oven and let cool slightly. Remove muffins from pan and let cool completely.

Quick & Easy Blueberry Muffins

2	cups	biscuit mix
1/3	cup	sugar
2	Tbsp	brown sugar (packed)
2	tsp	orange peel, grated
1		egg
2/3	cup	Carnation milk
2	Tbsp	vegetable oil
1	cup	fresh or frozen blueberries, thawed and drained
2	tsp	orange juice (optional)
2	Tbsp	sugar

Procedure

Preheat oven to 400°. Grease or paper-line 12 muffin cups.

Combine baking mix, granulated sugar, brown sugar and orange peel in large bowl. Beat egg lightly in small bowl; stir in evaporated milk and vegetable oil. Add evaporated milk mixture to baking mix mixture; stir just until moistened. Gently fold in blueberries.

Spoon batter into prepared muffin cups, filling 3/4 full. Gently brush tops with orange juice and sprinkle with granulated sugar.

Bake for 15-18 minutes or until wooden pick inserted in centre comes out clean.

Rosanna's Raspberry Muffins

Todd recalls, "On many special occasions I was able to visit Rosanna Tizzard who was the 2nd owner of George House with her husband Fred Tizzard. On one occasion we feasted on her delightful raspberry muffins and coffee. This recipe is reminiscent of those muffins. Today there are still raspberry canes on the George House property growing wild and those wild raspberries make such sweet muffins."

2 1/4	cups	flour
2	tsp	baking powder
1/2	tsp	salt
2	Tbsp	sugar
1		egg, lightly beaten
1	cup	cold milk
1/2	cup	butter, melted
1	cup	fresh raspberries

Procedure

Preheat oven to 375°.

Mix dry ingredients together in medium-sized bowl. In a small bowl blend egg, milk, and butter. Add to the dry ingredients and mix just until lumpy. Add raspberries, stirring gently.

Do not over-mix. Spoon into greased muffin tins.

Bake for 25-30 minutes.

Strawberry Rhubarb Muffins

This recipe is made best with locally grown rhubarb. We use Florence George's rhubarb. A few good rhubarb tips as follows: 1. Do not eat the leaves or roots as they are poisonous. 2. Rotted manure is excellent for a great rhubarb harvest. 3. At the first hard frost cut off all the rhubarb and toss into your compost. 4. For a healthy harvest the following year do not remove all of the rhubarb during the growing season.

2	cups	flour
1	Tbsp	baking powder
1/2	tsp	cinnamon
1/4	tsp	salt
1		egg
1/2	cup	brown sugar
3	Tbsp	strawberry jam
3/4	cup	milk
2	Tbsp	butter (no substitutes)
2	tsp	vanilla
1 1/2	cups	fresh rhubarb, diced

Procedure

Combine all dry ingredients except the brown sugar.

Whisk together brown sugar, egg, and jam, then whisk in butter and milk and vanilla. Stir in rhubarb. Pour mixture over dry ingredients and mix just to moisten ingredients.

Place in muffin cups about 2/3 full.

Bake at 400° until lightly browned and tested done, about 20-25 minutes.

George HOUSE

HERITAGE BED & BREAKFAST

SALADS, SOUPS, CHOWDERS & STEWS

Carrot Raisin Salad

We know this is an easy recipe, and it can be found at almost every summer potluck. So, if it's your turn to take something, why not this dish?

1 1/2	cups	raw carrot, finely shredded
1/2	cups	raisins
1/2	cup	celery, minced
1/2	cup	walnuts, chopped
1/4	tsp	salt
4	Tbsp	mayonnaise

Procedure

In a bowl combine all the ingredients, chill and serve best over lettuce leaves.

Creamy Potato Salad

10		medium potatoes, cooked, peeled and cubed
1	cup	celery, chopped
1/2	cup	onion, finely chopped
1/3	cup	sweet pickles, chopped
1 1/4	cups	mayonnaise
3	tsp	sugar
3	tsp	vinegar
2 1/2	tsp	yellow mustard
2	tsp	salt
6		hard-boiled eggs, coarsely chopped
		paprika for garnish (optional)

Procedure

In a bowl mix the chilled potatoes, celery, onion, and sweet pickles.

In a separate bowl combine the mayonnaise, sugar, vinegar, mustard, and salt. Mix well and then toss over the potato mixture and coat the potatoes well. Add the chopped eggs and mix again.

Sprinkle with paprika and chill before serving.

Celery Salad

1/4	cup	olive oil
		juice of 1/2 a lemon
1	tsp	dried mustard
	pinch	salt
1	bunch	celery, sliced

Procedure

In a bowl mix the olive oil, lemon juice, mustard and salt. Add the celery and toss well. Keep in fridge for at least overnight and serve well chilled. Toss before serving.

French Salad Dressing

1	cup	vegetable oil
1/2	cup	vinegar
1/3	cup	ketchup
2	tsp	paprika
4	tsp	onion, finely grated
		juice of 1/2 a lemon
2	tsp	salt
3/4	cup	sugar

Procedure

Mix all the ingredients in a bowl and then cover the bowl and chill in the fridge. Stir well before using.

Grow Dat Broccoli Salad

We've made this salad many times and the best has been when we were able to get fresh broccoli from Grow Dat's organic farm in Heart's Content.

1		head of broccoli, in floret bite-sized pieces
8		slices of bacon, cooked and reserve bacon fat
1/3	cup	vinegar
1/3	cup	brown sugar
1		onion, quartered and separated

Procedure

In a bowl add the broccoli florets and add the crumbled, cooked bacon. Sauté the onion pieces in the reserved bacon fat until tender.

Add the onion to the bowl leaving the bacon fat in the pan. Now add the vinegar and brown sugar to the pan and simmer for 5 minutes until mixture reduces and pour over the broccoli and onion, toss and serve.

Lunenburg Cucumber Salad

Dale says, "I spent quite a bit of time visiting Mahone Bay, Nova Scotia and had a variety of Lunenburg Salad as they called it. This is one version that I tend to like."

2		large cucumbers
1	tsp	salt
3	Tbsp	onion, finely diced
1/2	cup	sour cream
2	Tbsp	cider vinegar
2	Tbsp	sugar
	pinch	white pepper

Procedure

Peel and finely dice the cucumbers and put in a bowl and toss with the salt. Let sit for 30 minutes. Drain the cucumber in a sieve to remove all moisture.

Return the cucumber to the bowl and add the onion, mix the cider vinegar, sugar, sour cream and pepper. Stir well, chill and serve.

Mayonnaise

If you are stuck and don't have any mayonnaise on hand – then make your own. It'll taste better and serve you well in a pinch.

1/2	tsp	dry mustard
1	tsp	cold water
2		egg yolks
3	Tbsp	lemon juice
1 1/4	cups	vegetable oil
		salt, to taste
	pinch	cayenne

Procedure

In a bowl mix the mustard and water to make a paste and let rest for 10 minutes. Add the egg yolks, salt, cayenne pepper and 1/2 of the lemon juice and beat with a hand whisk or electric mixer. Gradually add 1/2 the oil in a drizzle into the mixture until it is all blended and then add the other half of the lemon juice. Now drizzle in the remaining vegetable oil until all is blended. Continue beating until a mayonnaise consistency.

Potato Egg Salad

While this may seem like a simple recipe, oftentimes we find if we wing it and don't measure the right amounts our potato salad can have too much mayo, be too salty or just off. Try making it from this recipe once and see the difference.

3	cups	potatoes, cooked and diced (cooled)
3		hard-boiled eggs, diced
1/4	tsp	salt
1/8	tsp	pepper
1	Tbsp	parsley, chopped
3/4	cup	mayonnaise

Procedure

In a large bowl combine potatoes, eggs, salt, pepper, parsley, and mayonnaise and mix together well. Chill and serve.

Opa Greek Salad

We love Greek salad and it can be best served when the ingredients come fresh out of your garden.

Salad

2		red onions, peeled and thinly sliced
3	Tbsp	cider vinegar
		salt to taste
3		large tomatoes, chopped
1		large cucumber, chopped
1		green pepper, finely diced
1	cup	Greek olives
2	cups	feta cheese, in cubes or crumbled

Dressing

1/4	cup	wine vinegar
1	tsp	dry mustard
1	tsp	sugar
1	cup	extra virgin olive oil
		salt and freshly ground black pepper

Procedure

In a large bowl mix all salad ingredients. In a separate bowl mix all the dressing ingredients and then slowly add the dressing to the salad tossing all the while until fully coated.

This salad is best served the first day well-chilled but is even better on the second day.

Todd's Stellar Caesar Salad

2		cloves garlic, peeled and crushed
5		anchovies, rinsed and patted dry
5		capers, drained
1	tsp	pepper
1/8	tsp	salt
1	tsp	Dijon mustard
1	Tbsp	Worcestershire sauce
1/2	tsp	Tabasco
3/4	cup	olive oil
1		raw egg
		juice of 1 lemon
2		heads Romaine lettuce
1/2	cup	real bacon bits
		croutons
3/4	cup	Parmesan cheese, freshly grated

Procedure

In a large bowl mash the garlic and anchovies with a large wooden spoon. Drizzle in the olive oil and continue to mash the garlic and anchovies until they are completely crushed.

Add the capers, pepper, salt, Dijon mustard, Worcestershire sauce, Tabasco sauce and remaining olive oil and mix well. Add raw egg and whisk the mixture in the bowl to completely incorporate the egg. Add lemon juice and continue to whisk.

Tear the romaine lettuce with your hands and place in separate bowl. Drizzle the Caesar salad dressing over the romaine and then top with bacon bits, cheese and croutons.

Recipe Tips

Don't cut salad greens with a knife as it can make them taste bitter – simply tear them up with your hands into bite-sized pieces.

Award-Winning Seafood Chowder

1	cup	butter
2		large onion, chopped
2		clove garlic, chopped
2	cups	potatoes, peeled and grated
1	cup	vermouth
4	cups	milk
4	cups	cream
1	cup	scallops, quartered, lightly poached
1	cup	shrimp, cleaned and heads removed, lightly poached
1	cup	codfish, lightly poached
1 1/2	cups	potatoes, peeled, cubed and cooked
1/2	cup	chives, chopped

Procedure

Melt butter in a large pot and add onions and sauté until soft. Add garlic and sauté until light brown.

Add grated potato, vermouth, milk, and cream and cook over medium heat so as not to scald the milk and cream. Cook for 20 minutes. Remove from heat and purée mixture in food processor or blender and add salt and pepper to taste.

Add cooked scallops, shrimp, and codfish and retained juices from poaching to the pot and incorporate the purée.

To the pot add the diced cooked potato and cook until they are warmed through. Use chopped chives as a garnish and perhaps even a sprinkle of paprika (although not necessary).

Recipe Tips

Make sure you use fresh fish and not salt cod. A touch of fennel powder also adds a nice touch to the seafood.

Broccoli & Cheddar Cheese Soup

1/2	cup	onion, chopped
1/4	cup	margarine
1/4	cup	white flour
3	cups	water
3	cups	broccoli
1	cup	fresh mushrooms, sliced
4	tsp	instant chicken bouillon granules
1	tsp	Worcestershire sauce
3	cups	cheddar cheese, shredded
1	cup	whipping cream
1	cup	milk

Procedure

In a large pot sauté the onion in the margarine. Stir in the flour, add water gradually, stirring and mixing well. Add the broccoli, mushrooms, bouillon and Worcestershire sauce and mix well. Cover and cook over medium heat until broccoli is tender. Stir in cheese, cream and milk. Cook until the cheese melts and soup is heated through, making sure not to bring soup to a boil.

Cold Cucumber Soup

3		cucumber, peeled, seeded and cut into 1/4″ cubes
2	cups	chicken stock or canned chicken broth
1	cup	sour cream
3	Tbsp	chives, chopped
2	tsp	fresh dill, minced
		salt to taste

Procedure

In a blender or food processor, combine cucumbers, 1 cup of chicken broth and a dash of salt. Cover and process until smooth in texture.

Remove the mixture to a large bowl and stir in the remaining chicken stock. Whisk in the sour cream, chives and dill, cover and chill well before serving.

Garnish with a few dill sprigs.

Carrot & Ginger Soup

2	Tbsp	butter
1		medium onion, finely chopped
1		celery stalk, diced
1		medium potato, peeled and cubed
1 1/2	lbs	carrots, diced
2	tsp	fresh ginger root, minced
5	cups	chicken stock
1/3	cup	whipping cream
1/4	tsp	nutmeg, ground
		salt and pepper to taste

Procedure

Combine butter, onion, and celery and cook until softened. Stir in potato, carrot, ginger, and chicken stock. Bring to a boil. Lower heat and cover pan and simmer for 20 minutes.

Pour soup into food processor and blend until smooth. Return soup to pot and warm. Stir in cream, nutmeg, and salt and pepper to taste.

Recipe Tips

When we serve this we increase the ginger a bit for a more robust flavour and it can be served with a small dollop of sour cream on top.

Cheddar Soup

1/2	cup	carrots, shredded
1/2	cup	celery, finely chopped
3/4	cup	boiling water
1/4	cup	onion, finely chopped
3	Tbsp	butter (no substitutes)
1/4	cup	flour
2	cups	milk
1 3/4	cups	chicken broth
1 1/2	cups	cheddar cheese, shredded (old-aged preferred)

Procedure

In a small pot add 3/4 cup of boiling water and carrots and celery. Cook until tender but not overcooked. In a large pot add the butter and cook the onion until tender. Stir in the flour to make a roux. Slowly add the milk and continue to cook until mixture thickens. Add chicken broth, and cheese to the other pot including the carrots, celery and water. Stir over low heat until the cheese is completely melted. Make sure not to bring to a boil or the soup will burn.

Clam Chowder

1 1/2	cups	clams
1	cup	onion, minced
1	cup	celery, minced
2	cups	potatoes, peeled and cut into 1/2″ cubes
3/4	cup	butter, melted
3/4	cup	flour
4	cups	cream, room temperature
2	Tbsp	red wine vinegar
1 1/2	tsp	salt
		pepper to taste

Procedure

Begin by draining the clams but reserve the liquid in a bowl. Combine the liquid and vegetables in a frying pan and add enough water to cover the vegetables. Simmer vegetables until tender crisp.

Blend the butter and the flour in a large pot and then whisk in the half-and-half gradually. Cook until thickened, whisking constantly.

Add the mixture from the frying pan, clams, vinegar and seasonings. Cook until heated through being careful not to bring to a boil.

Corn Chowder

Serve this hearty chowder on a chilly fall evening.

2	oz	butter
1		medium onion, finely chopped
3		stalks celery, diced
2		carrots, peeled and diced
2	Tbsp	flour
2	cups	chicken broth
4	cups	milk
2		medium potatoes, diced and boiled
3	cups	corn
		salt and pepper to taste

Procedure

Melt the butter in a heavy soup pot. Add the onion, celery, and carrots. Cook over medium heat just until soft. Sprinkle on the flour and cook for 3 minutes, stirring frequently. Stir in the broth. Stir in the milk. Heat until steaming. Add the cooked potatoes and corn.

Cook for 45-55 minutes over low heat. Check the seasoning. Serve warm.

Dale's Pea Soup

1	lb	salt beef
2	cups	split peas
2		onions, peeled and chopped
4		carrots, peeled and diced
4		potatoes, peeled and cut into 1/2″ cubes
1		small turnip, peeled and cut into 1/2″ cubes

Procedure

Begin by soaking the meat and peas in a large pot overnight in cold water. In the morning drain the pot and add 6 cups of water to the pot. Add the onions and bring the pot to a simmer and simmer for 2 hours. At the end of the simmering time add the carrot, potato and turnip and cook for an additional 30 minutes.

If the soup thickens up too much you can add a bit more water to the soup but don't overdo it.

Harvest Pumpkin and Parsnip Soup

Soup Ingredients

1	Tbsp	olive oil
1	Tbsp	butter
1		onion, chopped
1	cup	carrots, peeled and diced
1	cup	parsnips, peeled and diced
3 3/4	cups	vegetable base stock
1	cup	pumpkin

Soup Garnish & Finish

1/2	tsp	olive oil
1/2		garlic cloves, finely chopped
3	Tbsp	fresh parsley, chopped
		paprika, to taste

Procedure

Heat oil and butter in pan and fry onion for 2-3 minutes until soft. Add carrots, parsnips, stir and cover for 5 minutes. Add pumpkin and cook another 5 minutes.

Add vegetable stock and seasoning and bring to boil. Reduce heat, cover the pan and simmer for 40 minutes.

Cool soup then pour into blender or food processor and purée. If too thick add a bit of water or vegetable stock. Pour purée back into original pan and warm.

To garnish the soup, heat oil, garlic, and parsley for 2 minutes, add paprika and stir.

Ladle soup into bowls and put a nice swirl of garnish in each bowl. Serve with a smile.

Recipe Tips

You can make this vegetarian by following the recipe or you can substitute chicken stock for a different take on the same recipe.

Cream of Broccoli Soup

3/4	cup	potatoes, peeled and cut into 1/2″ cubes
1		medium carrot, thickly sliced
2	cups	broccoli, chopped
2	Tbsp	butter
2	Tbsp	flour
1 1/2	cups	milk
1/2	tsp	salt
	dash	nutmeg
	dash	white pepper

Procedure

In a large pot boil the potatoes and carrots, drain and set aside in a bowl. Cook the broccoli in the pot and then drain and add to the potatoes and carrots.

Melt the butter in the pot and then add the flour and stir until smooth creating a roux. Slowly add the milk and bring to a boil until the mixture thickens. Add salt, nutmeg and pepper and then stir. Add the potatoes, carrots and broccoli and simmer. Be sure not to boil the soup before serving. Only bring to a hot simmer.

Gambo Hamburger Chowder

1 1/2	lbs	beef, ground
3/4	cup	onion, chopped
1 1/2	cups	celery, chopped
1	clove	garlic, minced
4	cups	canned beans with pork
3	cups	water
3	cups	minestrone soup
1	Tbsp	Worcestershire sauce
1/2	tsp	oregano

Procedure

Brown your ground beef in a large pot with onion, celery and garlic, stirring frequently. Drain any excess fat from beef. Add all remaining ingredients, cover and simmer for 15 minutes.

Moratorium Cod Chowder

1	lb	fresh cod
1/2	cup	onion, finely chopped
1	cup	carrots, peeled and diced
3	cups	water
1/8	tsp	pepper
2	tsp	salt
1/8	tsp	sugar
2	Tbsp	butter (no substitutes)
2	cups	potatoes, peeled and cut into 1/2″ cubes
1	cup	celery, finely chopped
3/4	cup	Carnation milk

Procedure

In a pot add the onion, carrot, water, salt, pepper, sugar, butter, potatoes and celery. Bring to a boil until vegetables are cooked.

Reduce the heat to simmer and add the codfish and simmer for 30 minutes or until the fish is cooked and flakes apart easily. Add the milk and bring back to a warm simmer. Be careful not to boil the soup.

Lentil Soup

1	cup	lentils, rinsed
4	cups	chicken stock or canned chicken broth
1	cup	water
1/4	cup	dry red wine such as cabernet sauvignon
1 1/2	lbs	tomato, peeled and cut into chunks
1		carrots, peeled and thinly sliced
1		onion, chopped
1		celery stalk, diced
1		garlic clove, crushed
1/4	tsp	coriander, ground
2	tsp	fresh basil, chopped or 1 tablespoon dried basil, crushed
1		bay leaf
6	Tbsp	Parmesan cheese, freshly grated

Procedure

Rinse lentils well and toss any discoloured ones. Combine lentils, chicken stock, water, wine, tomatoes, carrot, onion, celery and garlic in large pot. Add coriander, bay leaf and basil.

Bring to boil, reduce heat to low, cover and simmer until the lentils are soft and tender – 30 minutes. Stir occasionally.

Remove the bay leaf, serve the soup into bowls and garnish with the Parmesan cheese.

Recipe Tips

Make this a vegetarian dish easily by using vegetable stock instead of chicken stock.

Mussel Soup

3	lbs	mussels
1		small onion, minced
1		carrot, diced
2		stalks celery, diced
3	cups	plum tomato, diced
3/4	cup	frozen corn niblets
1/2		green pepper, finely diced
1	cup	shrimp, cleaned and heads removed
2	cups	water
1	cup	white wine
2	cloves	garlic, freshly chopped
1	Tbsp	ginger, grated
1/3	cup	cilantro, chopped
2	Tbsp	curry powder
1/4	cup	butter
1/8	tsp	salt to taste

Procedure

In a large pot add white wine and bring to a boil and then quickly add the mussels and cover for 5 minutes or until the mussels have fully opened. Remove the mussels from the pot to a large bowl to stop the cooking process. Remove 2/3 of the mussels from the shells and toss the shells. Do not use any mussels that have not opened.

Put the liquid from the pot in a separate bowl and keep for use later in the recipe. In a small pot sauté the carrot, onion and celery in the butter for 4-5 minutes until tender. Add the garlic, ginger, and curry powder and sauté for an additional 2 minutes. Now add the tomatoes, water and simmer liquid and bring to a boil. Reduce the heat and keep at a simmer. Now add the shrimp, corn, and green pepper and continue to simmer for 5 minutes.

Add the mussel meat and simmer for a further 3 minutes. Season with salt and pepper according to your taste. Add the cilantro and the mussels in the shells and simmer for 2 more minutes.

Serve and enjoy.

Recipe Tips

When making a soup, sauce, or casserole that ends up too fatty or greasy, drop in an ice cube. The ice will attract the fat, which you can then scoop out.

Old Shop Soup

Years ago they harvested mussels in Old Shop, across the bay from Dildo. This recipe harkens back to those days.

1	cup	mushrooms, sliced
2	Tbsp	onions, minced
2	Tbsp	butter
2	Tbsp	flour
2	cups	chicken stock
1/2	cup	cream
1/2	tsp	salt
1/4	tsp	pepper
1/4	tsp	nutmeg

Procedure

In a large pot add the butter, onion and mushrooms and sauté for 5 minutes. Sprinkle the flour over the mushrooms and onions and stir. Add the chicken stock and stir until mixture thickens. Cool the mixture. Add the cream, pepper and nutmeg and mix well. Heat the soup without bringing it to a boil. Serve hot.

Pea Soup Doughboys

No pot of pea soup from Newfoundland is complete without a helping of doughboys in your bowl. Marina, Todd's mom, makes the best ones that we have ever had. While she doesn't measure and has the skill of a seasoned cook, we've broken the recipe down for you.

2 1/4	cups	flour
1	cup	cold water
1	tsp	salt
2	tsp	butter
3	tsp	baking powder

Procedure

In a large bowl mix your flour, baking powder and salt together. Cut in the butter and slowly add 1 cup of water until a dough mixture is attained. Remove enough dough to make a small ball – a small ice cream scoop is ideal for this. Form the ball and drop into hot pea soup about 15 minutes before you are ready to serve the soup.

Ladle the soup and then ensure that everyone gets 1 or 2 doughboys in their bowl.

Potato And Leek Soup

1/2	cup	onion, chopped
2	cups	leeks, chopped
2	Tbsp	butter
2	cups	potatoes, peeled and sliced
4	cups	chicken stock
		salt and pepper to taste
1		egg yolks, lightly beaten
2	cups	half-and-half cream
2	Tbsp	parsley, chopped

Procedure

In a pot sauté onion and leeks in butter for 15 minutes or until tender but not cooked to brown stage. Add the potatoes, chicken stock and salt and pepper to taste. Cook until potatoes are tender. Put mixture into a food processor or blender and process. Pour back into pot. Stir a small amount of the hot purée into the egg yolk and then slowly add that mixture back into the pot. Add the half-and-half cream while stirring. Heat to serve, ensuring to not bring soup to a boil. Garnish with parsley.

St. Pierre French Onion Soup

4		large onions, thinly sliced
2	Tbsp	butter
4	cups	beef stock
1	tsp	Worcestershire sauce
3		crusty rolls
1/4	cup	Parmesan cheese, grated
1/4	cup	mozzarella cheese, grated

Procedure

In a large pot add the butter and onions and sauté the onions until they are lightly browned. Add the beef stock and Worcestershire sauce and bring to a soft boil for 20 minutes. Taste the stock and season with any needed salt or pepper – being careful not to over-salt.

Pour the soup in ovenproof bowls and then put 1/2 a crusty roll on top of the soup and top with equal amounts of Parmesan and mozzarella cheese. Repeat for each of the other bowls. Put the bowls on a cookie sheet and put the oven on broil. Broil for a minute or so until the cheeses are melted. Serve while the cheese is still hot.

Route 80 Chili

2	Tbsp	olive oil
5		cloves garlic, minced
2		onions, diced
1 1/2	lbs	beef, ground
1/2	tsp	salt
1	tsp	black pepper, freshly ground
2	Tbsp	pure red chili powder
1	cup	Roma tomatoes, blanched, peeled and diced
1/2	cup	tomato paste
1/2	cup	beef stock
1	cup	dark beer
2	Tbsp	cider vinegar
3/4	tsp	cumin, ground
2	tsp	oregano, minced
1/4	cup	parsley, minced
2	cups	kidney beans, drained
1/2	cup	goat cheese, for garnish

Procedure

To prepare the chili, heat the olive oil in a large saucepan. Add the garlic and onions and sauté over medium-high heat for 5 minutes. Add the beef and sauté for 7 or 8 minutes longer, while stirring frequently, or until the beef is well browned on all sides.

Season with salt and pepper, stir in the chili powder, and cook for 2 minutes more. Add the tomatoes, tomato paste, beef stock, beer, vinegar, cumin, oregano, and parsley, and stir well to combine. Bring to a simmer, turn down the heat to low, and cook, covered, for 45 minutes.

Add the beans and cook for 15 minutes longer, stirring occasionally. Ladle into serving bowls and sprinkle with goat cheese.

Turkey Soup

Turkey is one of Todd's most favourite foods. Todd loves cooking turkeys as much as he does eating it. Needless to say we always have leftover turkey the next day and we use it for hot turkey sandwiches, turkey casserole and my favourite – turkey soup. This soup is ideal the day it's made and even better the next day, if there is any left over.

2	cups	turkey breast, cooked, cut into 1″x2″x1″ cubes
		water
2		chicken bouillon cubes
1	cup	celery, chopped
1	cup	carrots, chopped
1		onion, peeled and chopped
		salt to taste
		leftover turkey carcass, bones and skin (no meat)
		Bouquet Garni
8		peppercorns
1		bay leaf
4		whole cloves
		cheesecloth

Procedure

Take the cheesecloth and lay it flat and put the bay leaf, peppercorn and cloves in the middle and then gather up the cloth and tie it into a knot – known as a bouquet garni.

In a large pot add the turkey carcass bones and skin and the bouquet garni. Add enough water to cover and then add the two chicken bouillon cubes and bring the pot to a simmer and continue to simmer for 2 hours.

Cool the stock and then remove the skin, bones and bouquet garni. Strain the stock to ensure any bones or skin are completely gone.

Add the turkey meat and vegetables to the stock. Bring to a boil and then simmer until the vegetables are softened – salt to taste. Serve hot.

Recipe Tips

If your turkey skin was fatty there may be some fat rising to the top of the soup – simply put a slice of bread on top of the soup and it'll absorb the fat. Remove the slice of bread and continue cooking.

This recipe can also be used for leftover baked chicken. I also like the flavour of cilantro so a few tablespoons of chopped fresh cilantro will add a little bit of additional flavour.

Yvonne's Cabbage Soup

Dale says, "My sister Yvonne didn't cook very much and she is the only person I know that could boil corn on the cob and set it on fire. Of course she would often put something on the stove and then head off into the living room to watch her soap operas, leaving dinner to be scorched. She did make a wonderful diet soup and this is our version of it as she didn't use any soup bones in her recipe."

14	cups	water
4	lbs	soup bones
1		bay leaf
2	cups	cabbage, chopped
1	cup	onion, chopped
1	cup	turnip, peeled and cut into 1/2 cubes
2	cups	carrots, sliced into 1/4" rounds
1	cup	celery, chopped
1	clove	garlic, minced
1		beef oxo cube
1/8	tsp	allspice
1/8	tsp	pepper

Procedure

In a large pot add the water and beef bones and 1 Oxo cube. Bring to a boil and add onion, celery, bay leaf and garlic and continue to boil until vegetables are softened.

Remove the soup bones and add all remaining ingredients. Bring back to a boil and then lower to a simmer until ready to serve.

Old-Time Kitchen Beef Stew

3	Tbsp	vegetable oil
1		large onion, sliced
2		carrots, cut in chunks
1		stock celery, cut into 1/4″ cubes
1	oz	flour
3	Tbsp	paprika
2	lbs	stewing beef
2	Tbsp	tomato paste
1	cup	red wine
1 3/4	cups	beef stock
1		sprigs thyme
1		bay leaf
		salt and pepper to taste
3		medium potatoes, peeled and cubed
3	oz	button mushrooms, thinly sliced

Procedure

Preheat oven to 375°. Heat half the oil in large ovenproof casserole dish, add onion, carrots, and celery and cook until softened about 5 minutes. Remove vegetables and put in a bowl.

Combine flour and paprika in zip lock bag and add beef cubes and shake the bag to coat. Heat remaining oil and add the beef cubes and brown all sides for approximately 10 minutes. Return the vegetables to the pot and stir in tomato paste, red wine, stock, herbs and seasonings and bring pot to a boil.

Stir in the potatoes and cover and transfer pot to the oven and cook for 1 hour at 375°. Stir in mushrooms and cook for an additional 30 minutes. Remove bay leaf before serving.

Recipe Tips

Todd's mom used to add parsnips and turnip if she had it on hand, to make this dish even better.

Beginner Stew

2	Tbsp	olive oil
1 1/2	lbs	stewing beef, cut into chunks
2	cups	water
1/2	cup	ketchup
3	Tbsp	vinegar
3	Tbsp	brown sugar
2	cups	carrots, peeled and thinly sliced
1	cup	onion, chopped
		salt and pepper to taste

Procedure

In a Dutch oven heat the olive oil and then add the stewing meat. When meat is browned add the water, ketchup, vinegar and brown sugar. Stir well and cover. Bring to a slow boil and boil for 1 1/2 hours. Add the carrot, onion and salt and pepper. Stir well and then cover and boil gently for an additional 30 minutes.

Shrimp Cookery

1		onion, minced
2		garlic clove, minced
1	Tbsp	vegetable oil
1	lb	shrimp, peeled and deveined
1		bay leaf
1/2		small bell pepper, coarsely chopped
1	8 oz	can tomato paste
2/3	cup	water
2	cups	rice, hot (cooked)

Procedure

In a pan sauté onion and garlic in vegetable oil until they soften and begin to caramelize. Add the shrimp and cook a few minutes longer – stirring often.

Add the remaining ingredients and simmer for 1 hour. Serve over hot rice.

Cabin Beef Stew

1 1/2	cups	small shaped pasta, cooked
2	Tbsp	vegetable oil
1	lb	lean stewing beef, cut into 1″ chunks
3/4	cup	onion, chopped
9	cups	water, hot
3	Tbsp	beef-flavoured instant bouillon
1		large bay leaf
1	tsp	basil leaves
1/8	tsp	pepper
1 1/2	cups	carrots, sliced
1 1/2	cups	celery, sliced
2	cups	stewed tomatoes, undrained

Procedure

In large saucepan or Dutch oven, heat oil. Coat beef with flour. Add beef cubes and onion; cook until beef is browned. Add water, bouillon, bay leaf, basil and pepper. Bring to boil. Reduce heat; simmer, covered, until meat is tender, about 1 1/2 hours. Add carrots, celery and tomatoes. Cook 15 minutes longer. Remove bay leaf. Stir in pasta. Cook until pasta is tender, 10-15 minutes, stirring occasionally.

Gros Morne Beef Stew

Todd recalls, "A famous line that I'll never forget told by Mrs. Bridges from Upstairs Downstairs is 'A stew boiled is a stew spoiled.'"

1 1/2	lbs	stewing beef
2		onions, sliced
3	Tbsp	butter (no substitutes)
1		bay leaf
1 1/2	tsp	salt
1/4	tsp	pepper
1	tsp	caraway seed
1/4	cup	vinegar
1		small cabbage head, cut into wedges
1/4	cup	gingersnap cookies, finely crushed

Procedure

In a large pot add the beef, onion and butter and brown the beef. Add 3 cups of boiling water, bay leaf, salt, pepper and caraway seed. Bring to a boil, cover and simmer for 1 1/2 hours.

Add the vinegar and cabbage, cover and simmer for another 45 minutes. Remove the cabbage and put on the outside of a platter and put the stewing beef in the middle.

Soften the gingersnap crumbs in 1/4 cup of warm water and stir that into the pot with remaining liquid. Pour the sauce over the meat and enjoy!

White Bean and Mushroom Stew

2	Tbsp	olive oil
5	cups	fresh white mushrooms, sliced
1	cup	onion, chopped
1	tsp	garlic, minced
3/4	tsp	thyme, dried and crushed
3 1/2	cups	chicken broth
1 3/4	cups	stewed tomatoes, chopped
1/4	cup	dry white wine
4	cups	white cannellini beans, drained

Procedure

In a Dutch oven or large saucepot, heat oil until hot. Add mushrooms, onion, garlic and thyme; cook and stir until onion is very tender and mushrooms are slightly golden, about 7 minutes.

Add chicken broth, tomatoes with their liquid and wine; bring to a boil; cover and simmer to blend flavours, about 15 minutes.

In a small bowl, mash 1 cup of the beans until smooth; add to stew.

Stir in remaining beans, heat until hot. Serve immediately with a mound of steamed rice, if desired.

Elephant Stew

While it is not easy to find elephant at your local Fresh Mart, Dominion, or Sobeys it is well worth trying to find some to make this recipe. This is an ideal recipe to make for large family reunions, special homecomings, and if you are invited to a potluck at your local SUF Lodge.

2	rabbits
	salt and pepper to taste
1	elephant (medium-sized works best)
1	can of brown gravy (Heinz is good with this)

Procedure

Cut the elephant into bite-sized pieces. This should take you about 2 months. This is an ideal job for your mother-in-law when she butts her head in the kitchen and screeches out, "Can I help you?"

Add brown gravy to cover. Cook over kerosene fire for about 4 weeks at 465°.

This dish will serve about 3,800 people. If more are expected, 2 rabbits may be added – but do this if only necessary, as some people do not like to find hare in their stew.

Recipe given to us by: Anonymous

George HOUSE

HERITAGE BED & BREAKFAST

VEGETABLES & SIDE DISHES

Baked Potato

Dale says, "Mom used to make baked potatoes quite often in the late fall and winter. She said that you can't bake a new potato and that would be a crime anyway as a new potato is best boiled with the skin on and mashed on your plate. I've included this recipe as a reminder that a baked potato is a great alternative to always serving whole boiled or mashed potatoes. Enjoy!"

Procedure

Begin by rooting through your bag of potatoes and find uniform-sized potatoes – 1 for each person that you are going to feed.

Scrub the potatoes well and then towel dry. Put the potatoes in a big bowl and drizzle a bit of olive oil over the potatoes and then use your hands to ensure that all the potatoes are fully rubbed in olive oil.

Preheat your oven to 425° and put your potatoes directly on the oven rack for 50 minutes. Remove from oven and split the tops of the potatoes to allow some steam to escape and then serve.

Recipe Tips

If you have a roast or anything else in your oven and want to conserve energy, simply wrap your potatoes in aluminum foil wrap (shiny side in) and bake them for 1 1/2 hours in a 350° oven.

Cauliflower au Gratin

1		large head cauliflower
		salt and pepper to taste
1	cup	sour cream
1 1/4	cups	cheddar cheese, grated
2	tsp	sesame seeds, toasted

Procedure

Chop the cauliflower into florets, boil until tender (approximately 10-15 minutes) and then drain. Put half of the cauliflower in a 2-quart casserole dish. Sprinkle with salt and pepper and spread 1/2 of the sour cream and half of the cheese over the first layer. Repeat layers with more cauliflower, salt, pepper, cheese and sour cream. Top with a sprinkling of sesame seeds and bake uncovered for 15 minutes in a 350° oven.

Recipe Tips

To keep cauliflower white while cooking, add a little milk to the water.

Couscous Pilaf

1	Tbsp	olive oil
1	Tbsp	butter, unsalted
1		small onion, cut into 1/4″ dice
3/4	tsp	cumin, ground
	pinch	cayenne pepper
2/3	cups	couscous, or
1		10-oz box medium-grain couscous
1 1/4	tsp	salt
1/4	tsp	pepper, freshly ground
2	Tbsp	fresh flat-leaf parsley, coarsely chopped

Procedure

If using long-grain couscous you'll need 2 1/2 cups of boiling water. You can reduce the amount of boiling water to 2 1/4 cups if using regular couscous. Meanwhile, in a large saucepan, heat olive oil and butter over medium-low heat. Add onions and cook until lightly browned, about 8 minutes. Stir in cumin and cayenne pepper, and sauté for 1 minute more.

Stir in couscous, salt, pepper, and boiling water. Cover and simmer over low heat until tender and water is absorbed, about 10 minutes. Add parsley.

Recipe Tips

Microwave a lemon for 15 seconds and double the juice you get before squeezing.

Creamy White Beans

1	cup	dried white beans (cannellini beans), soaked overnight in water (cover, drain)
1		medium onion, halved
1		garlic clove, peeled and smashed
2		sprigs thyme
		coarse salt
		white pepper, freshly ground, to taste
1/4	cup	heavy cream
2	Tbsp	butter, unsalted, or herbed garlic butter

Procedure

In a medium saucepan, combine the drained beans, onion, garlic, and thyme. Add enough cold water to cover by 2". Bring to a boil over high heat. Reduce the heat to medium-low and simmer for 20 minutes. Season with the salt and continue cooking until the beans are just tender, about 15 minutes more, depending on the dryness of the beans. Drain the beans, reserving 1/2 cup of the cooking liquid.

Return the beans and the reserved liquid to the saucepan. Add the cream and bring to a simmer over medium heat. Cook until slightly thickened, about 5 minutes. Stir in the butter, and season with salt and pepper.

Curried Carrots

1	lb	carrots, peeled and cut into 1/2" slices
1	Tbsp	apricot jam
1 1/4	tsp	lemon juice
3/4	tsp	Dijon mustard
1	tsp	curry powder
1	tsp	butter, unsalted
2	tsp	vegetable oil
1 1/2	tsp	brown sugar
1/4	cup	raisins

Procedure

Place carrots in a steamer basket over boiling water. Cover saucepan and steam 5-7 minutes or until almost tender.

Remove carrots from steamer and set aside. Combine apricot spread, lemon juice, mustard and curry powder in a small bowl. Heat butter and oil in a heavy non-stick pan over medium high heat.

When oil is hot sauté carrots 1 minute. Stir in brown sugar and raisins and sauté another 1-2 minutes. Add spice mixture, stirring constantly 2-3 minutes, scraping down sides of skillet, or until carrots are glazed.

Dale's Baked Beans

1	lb	dried navy beans
2		onions, chopped
1/2	cup	brown sugar
1/4	cup	molasses
1/3	cup	ketchup
1/4	lb	bacon, diced
1	Tbsp	salt
1 1/2	tsp	dry mustard
1/4	tsp	pepper

Procedure

Soak beans in water overnight. Drain and put all ingredients in cooker. Add 1 cup water and stir to blend. Cover and cook on low 10-12 hours.

Can also spice it up with a few cloves of garlic, a half teaspoon of powdered ginger, and a good dash of Worcestershire sauce.

Recipe Tips

Bacon grease can be filtered through a coffee filter when hot or warm and then put in the fridge and used to grill vegetables.

Garlic Green Beans

1	Tbsp	butter
3	Tbsp	olive oil
1		medium head garlic, peeled and sliced
4	cups	canned green beans, drained
		salt and pepper to taste
1/4	cup	Parmesan cheese, grated

Procedure

In a large skillet over medium heat, melt butter with olive oil; add garlic, and cook until lightly browned, stirring frequently. Stir in green beans, and season with salt and pepper. Cook until beans are tender, about 10 minutes. Remove from heat, and sprinkle with Parmesan cheese.

Recipe Tips

The quickest way to chop parsley is to snip it with scissors.

Garlic Mashed Potatoes

4		medium potatoes, peeled and cubed
7		garlic cloves, minced
1/3	cup	milk, warmed
1/4	cup	sour cream
2	Tbsp	butter or margarine
		salt to taste
		white pepper to taste

Procedure

Boil the potatoes over medium heat until tender and drain them.

Add the garlic and mash the potatoes. Add the milk, sour cream, butter, salt, and pepper and mix well until smooth.

Recipe Tips

To keep potatoes from budding in the bag, put an apple in with them.

Potato Scallop

8		large potatoes, peeled and thinly sliced
1		small onion, chopped
4	Tbsp	white flour
1	tsp	salt
1	Tbsp	butter
1 1/4	cups	milk
1 1/4	cups	water

Procedure

Preheat your oven to 375°. Butter a casserole dish and scatter the onion across the bottom of the dish. Add a layer of the sliced potatoes to the dish to cover the bottom and then gently dust the potatoes with some of the white flour.

Continue to repeat the layering of potatoes and dusting of flour until all the potatoes are used up. If you still have leftover flour that is okay – don't use it.

Sprinkle salt over the top of the casserole and then pour the milk and water mixture over the potatoes until all the potatoes are covered. If there is leftover milk water mixture that is ok – don't use it.

Bake in the oven at 375° for 2 hours uncovered.

Recipe Tips

After boiling pasta or potatoes, cool the water and use it to water your house plants. The water contains nutrients that your plants will love.

Maple Glazed Carrots

1 1/2	lbs	baby carrots
3	Tbsp	butter (no substitutes)
1/2	cup	real maple syrup
1/2	tsp	salt
2	Tbsp	parsley, chopped

Procedure

Cook carrots in boiling water until almost tender and drain – but keep 1/4 cup of the water from the carrots.

Melt butter in a frying pan and roll the carrots in the butter. Add the reserved 1/4 cup of liquid, maple syrup and salt. Cook uncovered until liquid is thickened – approximately 10 minutes. Sprinkle with parsley and smile.

Roasted Potatoes With Garlic

8		medium potatoes
3	Tbsp	butter
2	tsp	garlic salt
1	tsp	black pepper
3	Tbsp	fresh parsley, chopped

Procedure

Peel and cut potatoes into bite-sized cubes. Rinse well and pat dry. Put butter in a large frying pan over medium to medium-high heat. Before the butter is completely melted add the potatoes. Cover and cook for 3-4 minutes. Remove the lid and ensure that the potatoes are browning and getting crispy. Check every few minutes and continue to turn them over from the bottom of the pan, rotating the potatoes so they don't burn. After the potatoes are browned, lower the heat to low and keep warm in the pan. Moments prior to serving, add the garlic salt, pepper, and parsley.

Recipe Tips

To make lighter and fluffier mashed potatoes, add a pinch or two of baking powder to the potatoes before whipping.

Ratatouille

1	Tbsp	olive oil
1	cup	onion, finely chopped
2/3	cup	green pepper, finely diced
1		garlic clove, chopped
1 1/2	lbs	eggplant, peeled and cut in 1/2″ cubes
1	lb	zucchini, unpeeled and cut in 1/2″ slices
1	tsp	basil
1	tsp	marjoram
3		medium tomatoes, peeled and quartered
1/2	tsp	salt
1/4	tsp	black pepper, freshly ground
2	Tbsp	Parmesan cheese

Procedure

Heat the oil in a large skillet and sauté the onion, bell pepper, and garlic for 3-4 minutes. Add all remaining ingredients except the Parmesan cheese, cover, and cook over medium heat, stirring occasionally, for about 10 minutes or until vegetables are tender-crisp. Garnish with cheese to serve.

Recipe Tips

Drinking cranberry juice and eating blueberries regularly will help stave off urinary tract infections.

Roasted Vegetables

1		small butternut squash, cubed
2		red bell peppers, seeded and diced
1		sweet potato, peeled and cubed
3		potatoes, cubed
1		red onion, quartered
1	Tbsp	fresh thyme, chopped
2	Tbsp	fresh rosemary, chopped
1/4	cup	olive oil
2	Tbsp	balsamic vinegar
		salt and freshly ground black pepper

Procedure

Preheat oven to 475° F (245° C).

In a large bowl, combine the squash, red bell peppers, sweet potato, and potatoes. Separate the red onion quarters into pieces, and add them to the mixture.

In a small bowl, stir together thyme, rosemary, olive oil, vinegar, salt, and pepper. Toss with vegetables until they are coated. Spread evenly on a large roasting pan.

Roast for 35-40 minutes in the preheated oven, stirring every 10 minutes, or until vegetables are cooked through and browned.

Recipe Tips

Remember veggies grown above ground should be boiled in salted water and those grown below ground in unsalted water.

Savannah's Fried Green Tomatoes

We've always wanted to try fried green tomatoes. Finally while visiting Savannah, Georgia, we were able to try them at Paula Deen's "The Lady and Sons" restaurant. They serve it on their menu with Vidalia onion relish and red pepper sauce – but I think they are also great with a bit of ranch dressing on the side. This is a great recipe to make while you are patiently waiting for the tomatoes to ripen on the vine!

2	Tbsp	vegetable oil
4		green tomatoes
1	cup	white flour
1	tsp	salt
1	tsp	pepper
1/8	tsp	paprika

Procedure

Cut your tomatoes into 1/2" slices. Mix the flour, salt, pepper, and paprika together in a glass pie plate. Dredge the tomato slices through the flour mixture to ensure it is fully coated. Knock off any excess flour.

In a frying pan add 2 tablespoons of vegetable oil, and when the pan and oil are hot add a few slices of tomatoes and fry for 3 or 4 minutes per side until golden brown.

Remove from the frying pan and transfer to a plate that has paper towel on it.

Repeat the frying step with the remaining slices and add a bit more vegetable oil if needed.

Serve warm or hot with your favourite condiment – ours is a bit of ranch or thousand island dressing.

Recipe Tips

Try using leftover filtered bacon fat to fry these in. It adds to the flavour and is a great use for the leftover fat.

Secret Agent's Creamy Mashed Potatoes

This recipe was given to me by a real estate colleague of mine and she got the recipe from her friend Elsie. I've made this recipe tons of times and you'll be really impressed by how rich the potatoes taste and how easy the recipe is.

6	large	potatoes, peeled and cut into 1/2" cubes
8	oz	sour cream
8	oz	cream cheese, softened
1	tsp	salt
1/2	tsp	white pepper

Procedure

Peel, cut and boil potatoes until softened. Drain potatoes well. Add the sour cream, cream cheese, salt and pepper and whip in a stand mixer or with a hand mixer until the mixture is lump free and the cream cheese is completely melted.

Pour into a greased or sprayed 3-quart baking dish. Cover with aluminum foil and bake at 325° for about 20 minutes. Remove from oven and serve.

Recipe Tips

You can add cheddar or Parmesan cheese at the last couple of minutes of baking to melt and make it more fun. Also, this is a great dish to bring to a gathering; simply make the potatoes the day ahead but don't bake them. The next day you simply put them in the oven for 30 minutes at 325° and they'll be piping hot and ready to serve. Finally, this is an excellent use of leftover mashed potatoes.

Sweet Potato Casserole

1	cup	all-purpose flour
2/3	cup	brown sugar (packed)
1/4	cup	pecans, toasted and chopped
1/4	cup	stick margarine, melted
1/2	tsp	cinnamon, ground
4		medium sweet potatoes, peeled and halved (about 2 1/2 pounds)
1/2	cup	granulated sugar
1 1/2	tsp	vanilla extract
1		large egg white
1	can	Carnation milk

Procedure

Preheat oven to 350°.

Combine first 5 ingredients in a small bowl. Set aside.

Place potatoes in a Dutch oven; add water to cover. Bring to a boil; cover, reduce heat, and simmer 30 minutes or until very tender. Drain well; mash in a large bowl. Stir in 1 cup of the combined ingredients, granulated sugar, vanilla, egg white, and milk. Spoon into a 2-quart casserole coated with cooking spray; top with remaining first mixture of combined ingredients.

Bake at 350° for 45 minutes.

Recipe Tips

We first had this dish on my travels in Savannah, Georgia – one of our favourite cities in the USA. This is a real staple in a Southern diet and can be found on many restaurant menus.

White Bean Ragout

5	cups	fresh mushrooms, sliced
3	Tbsp	oil
1	cup	onion, finely diced
1 1/2	tsp	Italian seasoning
3/4	tsp	salt
2 1/2	cups	white beans, rinsed and drained
2 1/2	cups	stewed tomatoes, undrained
1/4	cup	Parmesan cheese

Procedure

If mushrooms are large cut in halves. In a large skillet over medium heat, heat oil until hot. Add mushrooms, onion, Italian seasoning and salt; cook until mushrooms are tender, stirring occasionally, about 6 minutes.

Add stewed tomatoes and white beans to skillet; heat through. Stir in Parmesan cheese.

Recipe Tips

When using rice, keep in mind that 1 cup of uncooked long-grain white rice makes 3 cups cooked.

Zucchini Bake

4	cups	zucchini, grated
1 1/2	cups	Monterey Jack cheese, grated
4		eggs, beaten
2	cups	cheese cracker crumbs

Procedure

In a bowl, mix the zucchini, cheese, eggs and mix very well. Pour into a buttered or sprayed 3-quart baking dish and sprinkle the cheese cracker crumbs over the top.

Bake in a 350° oven for about 35 minutes. Remove and let cool for 5 minutes then serve.

Zucchini Patties

1 1/2	cups	zucchini, grated
1		egg, slightly beaten
2	Tbsp	flour
1/3	cup	onion, finely chopped
1/2	tsp	seasoned salt

Procedure

Heat a pan and add about 3 tablespoons of oil. Mix all the ingredients above and drop by the tablespoon into the frying pan at medium heat.

Turn and brown both sides. Remove each and drain on a couple of layers of paper towel. Serve hot and they are excellent with a dollop of sour cream.

Recipe Tips

When boiling vegetables cover those that grow underground and keep uncovered those that grow above ground.

George House

HERITAGE BED & BREAKFAST

MAIN DISHES

Beef Burgundy

Dildo was simply lovely. The room was lovely. The bed was lovely. The breakfast was lovely. Like what is there to say? The host knew the area inside out and seemed happy enough to see us and made us totally welcome. – Guest

1	cup	mushrooms, sliced
6		small pearl onions, cut into fourths
3	Tbsp	butter
6		slices of bacon, sliced and diced
1	lb	steak, cut into 1″ cubes
1	Tbsp	flour
1/2	cup	red wine
3/4	cup	beef broth
1		bay leaf
2		cloves garlic, minced
1/2	tsp	thyme, ground
1 1/2	cups	carrots, diagonally sliced
		salt and freshly ground black pepper
		package of egg noodles
1 1/2	Tbsp	parsley, chopped

Procedure

In a large skillet, sauté mushrooms and onions in hot butter until golden brown. Remove from skillet and set aside. Add bacon to skillet and fry until crisp; remove with a slotted spoon and reserve.

Add top sirloin steak to skillet and fry in bacon fat, stirring frequently, until well browned. Return mushroom and onion mixture to skillet and add flour; toss until flour disappears.

Add wine, beef broth, bay leaf, garlic and thyme. Simmer, covered, for 30 minutes, stirring frequently. Add carrots and cooked bacon, and cook covered, for 15 minutes longer.

Season with salt and pepper. Before serving, remove bay leaf. Serve over hot buttered noodles. Sprinkle with parsley.

Beef Stroganoff

I am from Newfoundland and being from Newfoundland I wasn't quite sure what to expect in a B&B but I had a great time. Dildo is a great little community to visit and the B&B is a great place to enjoy it from. – Guest

1	Tbsp	flour
1/2	tsp	salt
1	lb	sirloin beef, cut into 1/4" strips
2	Tbsp	butter
1	cup	mushrooms, sliced
1/2	cup	onion, chopped
1	clove	garlic, minced
2	Tbsp	butter
3	Tbsp	flour
1	Tbsp	tomato paste
1 1/4	cups	beef stock
1	cup	sour cream
2	Tbsp	sherry or dry white wine

Procedure

In a bowl combine 1 tablespoon of flour and the salt and mix together. Dredge the meat through the mixture and put on a plate.

Heat a frying pan and add the 2 tablespoons of butter. When the butter is melted add the sirloin strips and brown.

Add the sliced mushrooms, onion and garlic to the pan and cook for 4-5 minutes until the mushrooms and onions are softened.

Remove the mixture from the pan, add 2 tablespoons of butter to the pan and melt. Add 3 tablespoons of flour to the pan and mix well with the butter and then add the tomato paste. Slowly pour in the beef stock and cook, stirring all the while until the mixture thickens.

Return the meat and mushroom mixture to the pan and mix with the sauce. Stir in the sour cream and sherry and bring to a quick boil. Reduce heat to simmer and then serve over noodles or rice.

Recipe Tips

To slice meat into thin strips – as for Chinese dishes – partially freeze and it will slice easily.

Crock-Pot Osso Buco

4		veal shanks or lamb shanks
		flour
1		clove garlic, minced
3	Tbsp	olive oil
1	cup	consommé
1/4	cup	dry white wine
2	Tbsp	tomato paste
		rind of 1 lemon, cut into strips
3		small carrots, finely diced
1	Tbsp	parsley, finely chopped
1/4	tsp	dried marjoram, crushed
1/4	tsp	dried oregano, crushed
1/8	tsp	dried sage, crushed

Procedure

Roll shanks in flour; brown with garlic in hot oil in skillet. Add remaining ingredients to a Crock-Pot. Stir to mix well. Add the shanks and cover the Crock-Pot and cook on low for 10-12 hours until the shanks are tender. Garnish with parsley and serve over pasta.

Recipe Tips

White pepper is stronger than black pepper in a recipe – so if substituting only use about half as much.

Glazed Corned Beef

1-4	lbs	corned beef brisket
2	Tbsp	prepared mustard
1 1/2	tsp	creamed-style horseradish
2	Tbsp	red wine vinegar
1/4	cup	molasses

Procedure

In a slow cooker, cover corned beef with water. Cover and cook on low 10-12 hours or until tender. Drain corned beef; place on a broiler pan or ovenproof platter.

Preheat oven to 400°. In a small bowl, combine mustard, horseradish, vinegar and molasses. Brush on all sides of meat. Bake, brushing with sauce several times, about 20 minutes or until meat begins to brown. Cut into thin slices.

Recipe Tips

Most meats carve better if allowed to stand 10-15 minutes after being removed from the oven.

Cabbage Rolls

Dale recalls, "It was a special occasion when my mom would make cabbage rolls for dinner. I loved the cabbage rolls and especially the tomato 'liquor' that would be left behind in the pan. While we don't make these often enough they are a real treat on a cold fall or winter day."

1		cabbage, whole
1	lb	lean beef, ground
1/2	cup	minute rice
1		large onion, minced
3		cloves garlic, minced
		salt and pepper to taste
1/2	cup	mushrooms, minced
2	cups	can stewed tomatoes, undrained
2	cups	spaghetti sauce

Procedure

In a pot add the can of tomatoes and bottle of tomato sauce and simmer. Preheat your oven to 325°.

Take the cabbage and remove the core and wash the leaves. Put the separated leaves in large pot of boiling salted water until the leaves are soft. Drain the leaves and set aside.

In a bowl add the ground beef, rice, onion, garlic, salt, pepper, and mushrooms and mix well. Spoon about 1 tablespoon of the mixture into 1 cabbage leaf and roll the leaf.

Ladle enough of the sauce to cover a 9"x13" baking dish. Place the cabbage rolls in the baking dish and then cover the rolls with enough of the remaining sauce to fully cover the cabbage rolls. Don't worry if you don't use all of the sauce and some is left over.

Bake at 325° for 2 1/2 hours. Check on the dish every 30 minutes or so and if the cabbage rolls require more sauce then add as needed. If you run out of sauce you can use a little tomato juice.

Meat Loaf With Mushroom Sauce

Meat Loaf

2	lbs	lean beef, ground
3	cups	mushrooms, chopped
1		package dry vegetable soup mix
1/2	cup	seasoned dry bread crumbs
1/2	cup	milk
1		egg, lightly beaten

Mushroom Sauce:

1/4	cup	milk
2	Tbsp	cornstarch
2	Tbsp	butter
3	cups	mushrooms, sliced
1/3	cup	onion, chopped
2	cups	beef broth

Procedure

Meat Loaves:

Preheat oven to 350°. In a large bowl, combine beef, mushrooms, vegetable soup mix, bread crumbs, milk and egg until well combined.

Form into two loaves, 7"x5" each. Place loaves in a shallow baking pan with rack. Bake for 45 minutes.

Mushroom Sauce:

In a small bowl, combine milk and cornstarch; set aside. In a large skillet, melt butter over high heat. Add mushrooms and onion; cook and stir over moderate heat until mushrooms and golden, about 10 minutes.

Stir in beef broth and 1/2 cup water; bring to a boil. Stir cornstarch mixture into mushroom mixture in skillet. Cook over high heat, stirring constantly, until slightly thickened, about 1 minute.

New Brunswick Boiled Dinner

Dale says, "My mother used to serve this quite often for dinner and she would always plate the dinner and then add a gravy boat or creamer dish full of extra 'sauce' for us to pour over our dinner on our plates. This dish certainly brings back some very fond memories."

5	lbs	corned beef
10		medium-sized beets, peeled
3		parsnips, peeled and cut into large pieces
6		large carrots, scrubbed and cut into large pieces
3		turnips, peeled and quartered
10		small onions, peeled
6		medium-sized potatoes, scrubbed and quartered
1		head cabbage, cut into wedges
		Dijon-style mustard and prepared horseradish as condiments
2		medium onions, peeled and quartered and cooked with the meat
2		bay leaves
1	tsp	salt
10		black peppercorns (or more to taste)
1		clove garlic, peeled and chopped
4		whole cloves

Procedure

Place the corned beef along with the pickling liquid, onion and spices in a large pot and add enough water to cover it. Simmer for about 1 hour per pound, adding water as necessary to keep the beef covered.

Remove from the liquid, leaving the liquid in the pot, and place in a shallow baking dish or other container. Place a cutting board or other baking dish on top, and place several heavy weights (cans of food, cast iron cookware, etc.) on top to compress it.

Boil the beets in a separate pot for 30-45 minutes, until tender. Meanwhile add the parsnips, carrots, and turnips to the beef cooking liquid and simmer for 30 minutes. Add the potatoes and simmer for an additional 15 minutes, then add the cabbage wedges and simmer 15 minutes more.

Slice the beef and arrange with the vegetables on a large, deep platter, along with a generous amount of the cooking liquid.

Shepherd's Pie

Dale recalls, "This is an ideal fall or winter recipe. I can remember my mom making this and anxiously awaiting it coming out of the oven. Some people add shredded cheddar cheese in the last 5 minutes of baking for added flavour – still, I love the back-to-basic recipe as it is."

5		large potatoes
6		mushrooms, sliced
		salt to taste
2	Tbsp	butter or margarine
2	Tbsp	parsley, chopped
1	Tbsp	tomato paste
1	dash	milk
1	dash	Worcestershire sauce
1	pinch	white pepper
1	cup	canned beef gravy
1	lb	lean hamburger
1 1/4	cups	canned peas
1		large tomato, chopped

Procedure

Boil potatoes in salted water to cover. Drain, cool and peel. Mash in large bowl with butter and milk and season to taste with salt and pepper. Set aside.

Sauté beef until browned, stirring to keep meat crumbly. Season to taste with salt and pepper. Add tomatoes, mushrooms, parsley, tomato paste, Worcestershire and gravy. Stir to mix. Add peas and cook about 5 minutes. Turn mixture into casserole.

Spread potatoes evenly over meat. Bake at 400° 40 minutes until top is crispy brown.

Sirloin Roast

4	lbs	sirloin roast
2	Tbsp	flour
2	Tbsp	vegetable oil
		salt and pepper to taste
1		medium onion, peeled, cut in half and sliced thin
2		bay leaf
1		clove garlic, minced
1/2	cup	water, hot
8		small onions, cut in eighths
8		medium carrots, peeled and cut into 2″ lengths
8		medium potatoes, peeled and cubed
1 1/2	tsp	salt

Procedure

Dust the roast with the flour to cover it all over.

Using a Dutch oven add vegetable oil and heat to brown the roast on all sides. Add salt and pepper to taste. To the Dutch oven add the onions, bay leaves, garlic and water. Cover and cook in 350° oven for 1 1/2 hour or until tender.

Add carrots and potatoes and salt and then cover and cook for an additional hour or until vegetables and meat are cooked.

Remove the meat and vegetables to a serving tray and then reduce pan sauce to make an excellent gravy.

Recipe Tips

Tenderize pot roast or stewing meat by using 2 cups of hot tea as a cooking liquid.

Veal Parmigiana

Frommer's guidebook lists this as one of Newfoundland's best B&Bs. – Guest

3/4	cup	Italian-style bread crumbs
3/4	cup	Parmesan cheese
		salt
		pepper
1		egg, beaten
1/8	cup	water
6		veal portions, thawed and pounded
4	Tbsp	clarified butter
3		slices mozzarella cheese

Sauce

2	Tbsp	olive oil
1		small onion, chopped
2		medium cloves garlic, minced
1		(6 oz.) can tomato paste
1/3	cup	water
3 1/2	cups	canned tomatoes, crushed
1	tsp	basil
1	Tbsp	sugar

Procedure

Combine bread crumbs, Parmesan cheese and seasoning. Beat egg and combine with water. Dip veal into beaten egg, then coat with dry mixture. Quickly sauté and place on oven broiler. Top each piece with a slice of mozzarella cheese. Broil until cheese begins to bubble. Pour 1/3 cup of sauce on each serving.

Sauce

Sauté onion and garlic in oil until onion is translucent. Stir in tomato paste and water. Add tomatoes, basil, and sugar. Simmer covered for 1/2 hour.

FISH & SHELLFISH

Basic Fried Fish

Todd recalls, "My mom would serve our family fish several times a week. One of her most common ways to serve it was this fried fish recipe. Try it out and you'll see why."

2	lbs	boneless fish fillets
1	cup	cornflakes, crushed
1/2	cup	water
1/2	cup	evaporated milk
1	Tbsp	salt

Procedure

Preheat your oven to 500°.

Put the crushed cornflakes in a pie plate.

In a bowl mix the salt, milk, and water. Stir to dissolve the salt completely. Dredge the fish fillets through the milk bath and then roll them in the crushed cornflakes.

Bake on a cookie sheet in a 500° oven for 15 minutes.

Boiling A Lobster

While this is a quick and easy recipe for boiling lobster I can still remember having to look up how to do this in a cookbook. If you can get live lobster from a local fisherman or at your supermarket then do buy them and try boiling your own lobster – you'll love the fresh taste. One of our favourite places to get lobsters in Nova Scotia is at Fisherman's Village in Eastern Passage, Nova Scotia. They'll steam them for you or you can take them home live. Make sure you have some drawn butter to enjoy the lobster with, and fresh baked rolls – and my favourite, a cold beer.

Procedure

In a large pot add cold water and lots of salt (sea salt preferred) and bring the water to a boil. Make sure the pot is large enough for you to be able to fully immerse the lobsters that you wish to cook.

Drop the live lobsters head first into the boiling salted water and bring the water back to a boil. Reduce the heat and simmer the lobster for 20 minutes.

Remove the lobster from the pot with a pair of tongs. Use a sharp knife and mallet to break the lobster shells and serve with warm drawn butter.

Broiling A Lobster

We love lobster any way we can cook it. While boiled lobster is very popular, I've had it broiled and love it and even had it done on a barbecue in the Caribbean. Try broiling it for something different – the recipe is easy and the results are delicious.

Procedure

Put your live lobster on a wood cutting board and put the lobster on its back. With a very sharp knife split the lobster tail from the body. This essentially kills the lobster.

Now take your knife and split the body in half down the centre lengthwise. Remove the dark vein on the back of the lobster.

Turn on your broiler. Place the lobster with meat side up and brush the meat with melted butter. Put on broiler for 15 minutes and then remove and serve hot with more melted butter.

You can add a little finely grated Parmesan cheese to your melted butter when you brush the meat before putting it under the broiler for added flavour.

Cod au Gratin

We spent two nights at the Inn By the Bay in Dildo NL, what an absolute treat! – Guest

1	lb	codfish
1/4	lb	butter
1/4	cup	flour
1 1/4	cups	milk
1	tsp	salt
1		small onion, chopped
1/2	cup	bread crumbs
1/2	cup	cheddar cheese, grated
		pepper to taste

Procedure

Preheat your oven to 375°.

Lay out the fish fillets and pieces on a greased ovenproof baking dish.

In a pot melt the butter, stir in the flour until smooth in texture and remove the pot from the heat, making a roux. Stir in 2/3 cup of the milk and return the pot to the heat and beat until smooth and the milk is incorporated. Add the remaining milk and again mix until smooth. Once smooth add salt, pepper, and onions. Cook on low heat for 5 minutes.

Pour the sauce over the fish fillets and sprinkle with bread crumbs and cheddar cheese. Bake for 20-30 minutes until the fish is cooked.

Recipe Tips

Thaw fish in milk for fresher flavour.

Codfish Fillet Rolls

We then sat on the deck and enjoyed a glass of wine and read as the day was sunny and it was great to see the boats as they passed by. – Guest

2	lbs	cod fillets
2		medium onion, finely chopped
1/4	cup	butter (no substitutes), softened
2	cups	fresh bread crumbs
1/2	cup	parsley
2	tsp	salt
1/2	tsp	nutmeg
2		eggs, beaten
2	Tbsp	butter, melted
1	Tbsp	lemon juice
1/8	tsp	paprika
		parsley to garnish

Procedure

Ensure that your cod fillets are individual serving-sized pieces. If the fillets are extra large cut them to individual serving sizes. Preheat your oven to 350°.

In a pan sauté the onions in butter until tender but not browned. Stir in the bread crumbs, parsley, salt, nutmeg and eggs. Divide the mixture evenly between the fish fillets and spread mixture over top of each fillet.

Roll the fillets lengthwise and secure them with a toothpick. Place the fillets seam side down on a glass baking dish. In a bowl mix the melted butter and lemon juice and drizzle evenly over the fish fillet rolls. Sprinkle with paprika. Bake uncovered in a 350° oven for 25 minutes.

Garnish with lemon wedges and sprinkled fresh parsley.

Fish Plant Crab Cakes

There is nothing better than making these crab cakes when you can get fresh crab. There are two great fish plants in New Harbour, Higdon's Fish Plant and Woodman's Fish Plant, just a couple of miles away. It is fun to watch the crab boats as they arrive during crab season. We have hosted many crab buyers at the B&B from all over, including China and Japan.

1/2	cup	onion, finely diced
1/4	cup	butter
1/2	cup	mashed potato
1		egg
1/4	cup	sour cream
1/4	tsp	cayenne pepper to taste
		pinch of salt
2		stalks green onion, finely chopped
1/2	tsp	Worcestershire sauce
1/2	lb	crab meat
1	tsp	garlic clove, minced
		parsley, minced

Procedure

Sauté onion in butter until soft but not brown. Mix all the remaining ingredients together and form into cakes.

Brown the cakes in a non-stick frying pan with 2 tablespoons of vegetable or canola oil. Serve hot.

Halibut in Wine Sauce

This lovely B&B located in the picturesque town of Dildo, Newfoundland, is beautifully decorated. Todd, the chef and owner will go out of his way to make you feel at home. The dining area looks out onto the bay where you may be lucky enough to see a whale . Food is very good and when ready to leave you'll get a bag of homemade cookies for the road. – Guest

1/4	cup	butter, melted
2	Tbsp	lemon juice
1/2	tsp	salt
1/4	tsp	pepper
2	lbs	Halibut steak
3	Tbsp	white flour
2	Tbsp	butter, melted
1/2	cup	dry white wine
1	tsp	lemon juice
1	cup	milk or cream
1/2	tsp	salt
1/4	tsp	pepper

Procedure

Preheat oven to 350°. Blend the 1/4 cup butter, 2 tablespoons of lemon juice, 1/2 teaspoon of salt, and 1/4 teaspoon of pepper in a bowl. Turn the oven to broil.

Place the fish on a sprayed broiler pan and brush with half of the mixture from the bowl. Place in the oven and broil for 5 minutes on each side and brush with remaining butter mixture when you turn the fish over. Remove from the broiler pan and place fish in a sprayed baking dish. Turn oven back to 350°. In a pot blend the flour and the 2 tablespoons of butter, stir in the wine and all remaining ingredients. Cook until thickened stirring constantly. Pour the wine sauce over the fish and bake in the 350° oven for 50-60 minutes or until done.

Mussels Marinara

Both Todd and Dale are very nice people and the review I gave them can't explain the feeling that you have when you leave. I would recommend this spot to any couple who wishes to go away and have a relaxing weekend or break. Thanks to the staff for our wonderful stay. – Guest

1	lb	mussels in shell
1	Tbsp	olive oil
1		medium onion, finely chopped
1	Tbsp	garlic clove, minced
1	Tbsp	tomato paste
2	Tbsp	red wine
2	cups	tomatoes, crushed
1	tsp	fresh basil, chopped
1	tsp	fresh oregano, chopped
1		bay leaf
		salt and pepper to taste

Procedure

In a large pot sauté the onion and garlic in olive oil until they are tender but not browned. Add the tomato paste to the pot and cook for 2 minutes. Add 1 tablespoon of the wine, tomatoes, basil, oregano, and bay leaf.

Simmer for 20 minutes and then remove the bay leaf. In a separate pot steam the mussels in a small amount of water for 8 minutes.

Once they are steamed, remove the mussels from the pot with a slotted spoon and put them in serving bowls. Pour the marinara sauce over the steamed mussels.

⁓ Newfoundland Crab Cakes ⁓

The breakfast they serve is awesome and has more food then I have ever had at breakfast. They have a great idea of handing out cookies in the morning to all their guests. – Guest

1	lb	crab meat from Newfoundland
1		egg, beaten
1	tsp	Dijon-style mustard
2	tsp	prepared horseradish
2	tsp	Worcestershire sauce
8		chives, snipped or onion, minced
3	Tbsp	fresh parsley, chopped
3	oz	bread crumbs
		salt and pepper to taste
1	Tbsp	whipped cream (optional)
2	oz	dry bread crumbs
1 1/2	oz	butter
		lemon wedge

Procedure

In a bowl mix crab meat, egg, Dijon mustard, horseradish, Worcestershire sauce, chives, parsley, fresh bread crumbs, and seasoning. Mix well. If mixture is too dry then add a little of the cream.

Divide the mixture into 6 portions and shape into small cakes. Add the dry bread crumbs to a plate and coat the cakes all over.

Melt the butter in a non-stick frying pan, fry the cakes until golden brown about 3 minutes a side. If needed add a bit more butter to make them more golden. Serve with a lemon wedge.

Recipe Tips

We love this with fresh Newfoundland crab, however, you can use canned crab in the off-season. This is also nice with a homemade hollandaise sauce and served for breakfast.

Oceanside Seafood Curry

This is an older house that has been remodelled beautifully. The owners are very helpful in any way that they can be. They have a quiet spot and I bet in the summer, with a cool breeze off the harbour, you would feel like you're in another world. – Guest

4	cups	rice, hot (cooked)
1 1/2		Granny Smith apples, diced
1		medium onion, chopped
1	cup	dried apricots, chopped
1/2	cup	raisins
2	cups	whipping cream
1 1/2	cups	dry white wine
3		clove garlic, chopped
3	Tbsp	curry paste
1	lb	scallops
1	lb	shrimp

Procedure

Cook rice as per directions on bag/box and keep warm. A rice cooker is a great tool to make rice and keep it warm.

In a pot sauté the garlic and onion in a bit of canola oil. When softened add raisins, apricots, and wine. Bring to a boil.

Add the whipping cream and curry paste and bring to a boil again (you can increase or decrease the amount of curry paste according to taste). Add rinsed shrimp and scallops and bring to a boil yet again and boil for 3 minutes – do not boil any longer or seafood will become rubbery.

Remove from heat and serve over warm bed of rice.

Recipe Tips

We've made this with lobster and crab as well as chicken so try the different variations.

Oh So Easy Coquille St. Jacques

Dale and Todd have a wonderful sense of humour and a genuine love for their business – it is a true passion to them and it shows in every little attention to detail offered to guests. Loved it and would love to return one day. – Guest

1	lb	scallops
2	Tbsp	butter
1/2	cup	fresh mushrooms, sliced
1/2	cup	green onion tops, chopped
1/2	cup	mayonnaise
1/4	cup	white flour
1/2	tsp	salt
1/8	tsp	pepper
2	cups	milk
2	tsp	lemon juice
1/2	cup	Parmesan cheese, grated

Procedure

Preheat your oven to broil. In a hot skillet sauté the scallops in butter. Add the mushrooms and onion and cook until the scallops and vegetables are tender.

Heat the mayonnaise in a small saucepan. Add the flour and seasonings. Gradually add the milk and lemon juice. Continue cooking until sauce thickens.

Add the scallop mixture to the sauce and mix thoroughly and then spoon into six individual dishes. Sprinkle Parmesan cheese over the dishes and then put the dishes in the oven under the broiler until lightly browned.

Snow Crab Pie

The rooms were beautifully furnished and the intimate dining room on the water's edge with superb food and wine makes for a perfect getaway not too far from St. John's. – Guest

1/2	lb	fresh crab meat or drained canned crab meat
1/2	cup	cheddar cheese, grated
1/2	cup	package cream cheese, softened
1/4	cup	green onion, sliced
1/4	cup	pimentos, diced
1	cup	milk
1/2	cup	baking mix such as Bisquick
2		eggs
		salt to taste
	dash	nutmeg to taste

Procedure

Preheat your oven to 350°. In a large bowl mix together the crab, cheddar cheese, cream cheese, green onion and pimentos.

In a food processor or blender combine the milk, baking mix, eggs, salt and nutmeg. Blend the mixture on high speed for 15-20 seconds then combine with the crab mixture. Spoon the mixture into a greased casserole dish. Place the casserole dish in a pan of hot water and bake for 40 minutes.

Lemon Pepper Salmon

This recipe while being very simple is one that has been made by us over 1,000 times. Guests love it and always ask for the recipe. The mayonnaise keeps the fish moist and the lemon pepper and dill provides a zesty flavour. A guest named Glynnis gave us this recipe for which I am forever grateful.

6		salmon fillets
1/2	cup	mayonnaise
		lemon pepper – see procedure
		dill – see procedure
		juice of 1 lemon

Procedure

Place salmon fillets in a sprayed 9"x13" glass baking dish. Sprinkle lemon juice over the fillets. Using a spatula gently spread the mayonnaise over the tops of the fillets creating a light coating – enough mayonnaise to cover the flesh.

Sprinkle lemon pepper over the fillets and then the same with dill.

Bake in a 350° oven for 25 minutes and serve hot.

Sole Fillet In Sour Cream

Dale, Todd and staff make you feel so welcome from start to end. I had no transport and they picked me up from Whitbourne Junction and Dale even took me on tour around the peninsula – generosity way beyond expectations. – Guest

4	tsp	butter (no substitutes)
2	lbs	sole fish fillets
1	tsp	salt
1	Tbsp	paprika
1/2	tsp	Tabasco sauce
1	cup	sour cream
1/4	cup	Parmesan cheese
1/4	cup	bread crumbs
1		lemon, sliced

Procedure

Preheat the oven to 350°. Grease an ovenproof casserole dish with 1 teaspoon of butter. Place fish on the bottom of the dish.

In a bowl add the salt, paprika, Tabasco sauce, and Parmesan cheese. Add the sour cream and mix again. Spread this mixture over the fish.

Top the fish with sprinkling of bread crumbs and dot with remaining butter. Bake uncovered for 30 minutes.

Serve with sliced lemon.

South Dildo Scallop Bake

The hospitality, warmth, rooms, dining, food, and service cannot be overstated. – Guest

1	lb	raw scallops
1	cup	rice (cooked)
		salt and pepper to taste
1		large onion, sliced
1		green pepper, seeded and thinly sliced
1	cup	mushrooms, sliced
1	cup	frozen peas
1/2	cup	bread crumbs
2	Tbsp	butter

Sauce

4	Tbsp	butter
3	Tbsp	white flour
1 1/4	cups	milk
1/4	tsp	salt
1/8	tsp	pepper
1/2	cup	cheddar cheese, grated

Procedure

Preheat your oven to 375°. In a frying pan sauté rice and onions and then add the green peppers and mushrooms.

In a saucepan melt the butter and then add the flour to create a roux. Remove from heat and gently add 3/4 cup of the milk, all the while stirring constantly.

Return the saucepan to the heat and thicken. Beat until the mixture is creamy. Gradually add the remaining milk, salt and pepper and stir for an additional 3 minutes. Remove the saucepan from the heat and add the cheese and stir until the cheese is all melted into the sauce.

Place the rice and vegetable mixture in the bottom of a casserole dish. Add the peas on top. Season well with salt and pepper. Place the scallops on the vegetables and cover with the cheese sauce.

Melt the butter and add the bread crumbs. Sprinkle this mixture over the sauce.

Bake for 20 minutes and remove and let rest for 5 minutes and then serve.

Fettuccini Alfredo

The beds are very comfortable, the rooms are quiet and well-furnished. The bathroom came with a cute rubber ducky. Sweet! And the best part? They sent us off with a package of cookies fresh from the oven. Can't wait to go back! – Guest

1	lb	fresh linguine
1	cup	heavy cream
3	Tbsp	butter, softened
		salt to taste
		pepper to taste
		nutmeg to taste

Procedure

Bring a large pot of salted water to a boil. Add the pasta and cook until it is tender but still firm to the bite, about 3 minutes. Drain and dry the linguine and set aside. In a saucepan place 3/4 cup of the heavy cream and butter. Cook over medium heat just to thicken.

Add linguine to the saucepan, and toss to coat. Add remaining 1/4 cup of cream and Parmesan cheese. Season to taste with salt, pepper, and nutmeg. Transfer to a serving dish, and serve immediately.

Macaroni & Cheese

Macaroni & Cheese is a real staple food – not only in the Southern USA, but everywhere. We love it, and especially this homemade version. Try it and you'll fall in love.

1 2/3	cups	elbow macaroni, cooked and drained
2	Tbsp	cornstarch
1	tsp	salt
1/2	tsp	dry mustard
1/4	tsp	black pepper, ground
1	can	Carnation milk
1	cup	water
2	Tbsp	butter or margarine
2	cups	cheddar cheese, grated

Procedure

Preheat oven to 375°. Grease 2-quart casserole dish.

Combine cornstarch, salt, mustard and pepper in medium saucepan. Stir in evaporated milk, water and butter. Cook over medium-high heat, stirring constantly, until mixture comes to a boil. Boil for 1 minute. Remove from heat. Stir in 1 1/2 cups cheese until melted. Add macaroni; mix well. Pour into prepared casserole dish. Top with remaining cheese.

Bake for 20-25 minutes or until cheese is melted and light brown.

Recipe Tips

A tablespoon of butter in a pot of boiling macaroni will keep it from boiling over or sticking to the bottom.

Macaroni & Tomato Bake

We originally only planned on one night, but we loved it so much we begged for a second night. – Guest

2	cups	elbow macaroni, uncooked
2		ripe tomatoes, sliced
2	Tbsp	butter (no substitutes)
1	Tbsp	flour
1/4	tsp	dry mustard
1/2	tsp	salt
2	cups	skim milk
2	cups	cheddar cheese, grated
1/2	cup	fresh bread crumbs

Procedure

Prepare pasta according to package directions; drain in colander. Preheat oven to 375°.

Slice the tomatoes into 1/2" thick slices. Set aside on a small plate.

Crumble the bread crumbs with your fingertips. Set aside on another small plate.

Into a 2-quart saucepan over medium heat, melt the butter or margarine. Add the flour, dry mustard and salt, then cook together for 2-3 minutes. Add the milk little by little and continue stirring until mixture thickens. Add cheese and stir until melted.

Place 2 slices of tomato in bottom of pan, then half the pasta. Place another 2 slices of tomato, the remainder of the pasta, and pour the sauce over all.

Arrange 3 slices of tomato on top and sprinkle with bread crumbs. Bake for 20 minutes. Serve immediately.

Mrs. George's Mac & Cheese

Would move in for good if the winters weren't so cold!! Todd, Dale, and Shaelie make you feel totally at home. The food is to die for, the rooms are luxurious, and the atmosphere is PERFECT!! I have absolutely ZERO negatives to say about this very special find. – Guest

1	cups	elbow macaroni, uncooked
1/4	cup	butter
4	Tbsp	flour
2	cups	milk
3/4	cup	cheddar cheese, grated
3	Tbsp	fresh parsley, chopped
		salt and pepper to taste
1/2	cup	dry bread crumbs
1/4	cup	Parmesan cheese, freshly grated

Procedure

Preheat oven to 350° and spray an ovenproof dish. Cook the elbow macaroni in boiling, very well-salted water just until tender. Drain well.

Melt butter in a saucepan, add the flour and cook for 2 minutes stirring all the time. Stir in the milk and then bring to a boil again stirring constantly and simmer until thickened – approximately 5 minutes.

Take the pan off the heat and add the macaroni, cheddar cheese, and parsley. Mix very well. Season to taste with salt and pepper. Pour mixture into ovenproof dish. Mix the bread crumbs and Parmesan cheese and then sprinkle evenly over the macaroni.

Bake in the oven until the top is a nice golden brown and the mixture bubbles up – approximately 30 minutes.

Mt. Scio Noodle Bake

On the first night we stayed in the George House on the Hill. The room was small but beautifully decorated with fabric-covered walls, antiques, luxury toiletries, high-thread bedding and even robes and slippers. – Guest

2	Tbsp	vegetable oil
4	Tbsp	butter (no substitutes)
2		onions, chopped
1		clove garlic, minced
2	cups	canned tomatoes, diced
		pepper to taste
1/4	tsp	Mt. Scio savoury
1		bay leaf
1/8	tsp	salt
3	cups	cheddar cheese, grated (old tastes best)
8	oz	package egg noodles

Procedure

In a pan combine the oil and 2 tablespoons butter and melt butter over low heat. Add the onions and garlic and sauté until tender.

Add the tomatoes, salt, pepper to taste, Mt. Scio savoury, and bay leaf to the pan. Cook over medium heat for 15 minutes and then remove bay leaf.

Cook the egg noodles in a pot of well-salted water as per package directions. Drain and add remaining 2 tablespoons of butter and 3 cups cheddar cheese, sauce and stir well. Pour into a sprayed ovenproof dish, sprinkle remaining cheese over top and bake at 350° for 30 minutes and the remove from oven and serve.

Our Own Fettuccine Alfredo

Todd and Dale were wonderful hosts, very welcoming and helpful. – Guest

1	lb	fettuccine
6		egg yolks, lightly beaten
2	cups	cream
1/4	cup	butter
1	cup	turkey meat, cooked and cut into cubes
		black pepper, freshly ground, to taste
		salt to taste
1/2	cup	Parmesan cheese, freshly grated

Procedure

Cook fettuccine in boiling salted water until tender. Drain.

In a medium bowl, blend egg yolks and cream together.

Place butter in a sauté pan and melt, add turkey and brown lightly. Add cooked fettuccine and heat through.

Add the egg/cream mixture and gently fold in until all the liquid is used.

Season to taste with pepper and salt. Add grated Parmesan cheese.

Quick & Easy Lasagna

Todd and Dale were extremely hospitable. With a baby we did need to have some items that needed to be refrigerated, and again this was not a problem at all. We were very grateful for their accommodating our needs.
– Guest

3/4	lb	hamburger
2 1/2	cups	bottled spaghetti sauce
6		lasagna noodles
1 1/2	cups	cottage cheese
1 1/2	cups	mozzarella cheese, coarsely shredded
2	Tbsp	Parmesan cheese, grated

Procedure

Cook meat in a large pan over medium-high heat until no pink colour is left in meat, stirring occasionally with a wooden spoon and breaking up the meat. Remove pan from heat. Place colander over bowl. Spoon meat into colander and let fat drain into bowl. Return meat to pan. Put fat in a container to throw away.

Spoon 1 cup of the spaghetti sauce in the bottom of a 2-quart rectangular baking dish. Stir remaining spaghetti sauce into meat in pan. Cook over medium heat until hot, stirring occasionally with a wooden spoon. Remove meat mixture from heat.

Place 2 uncooked noodles on sauce in bottom of dish. Spread 1/3 of the meat mixture on top of noodles. Spread 3/4 cup of the cottage cheese over meat. Sprinkle 1/2 cup of the mozzarella cheese over cottage cheese. Add another layer of 2 uncooked noodles, 1/3 of the meat mixture, the rest of the cottage cheese, and 1/2 cup of the mozzarella cheese. Layer remaining uncooked noodles, meat mixture, and mozzarella cheese. Finally, sprinkle Parmesan cheese over top, if you like.

Cover baking dish with foil. Bake in a 350° oven for 1 hour. Remove from oven and let stand on a cooling rack with foil cover in place for 15 minutes.

Standard Lasagna

The young woman who waited on us every morning was extremely friendly and attentive to our needs. She seemed to genuinely enjoy her job and the guests at the B&B. – Guest

1	lb	sausage meat
1		clove garlic, minced
1	Tbsp	whole basil
1 1/2	tsp	salt
2	cups	canned tomato, diced
1 1/3	cups	tomato paste
1	box	lasagna noodles
3	cups	ricotta cheese
1/2	cup	Parmesan cheese, grated
2	Tbsp	parsley flakes
2		egg, slightly beaten
2	tsp	salt
1/2	tsp	pepper
1	lb	mozzarella cheese, coarsely shredded

Procedure

Begin by browning sausage meat in pot, remove any fat. Add garlic, basil, salt, tomatoes, and tomato paste. Simmer uncovered for about 30 minutes stirring often.

Cook lasagna noodles or use no-bake noodles and follow package directions.

Mix ricotta cheese, parsley flakes, eggs, salt, and pepper. Begin by laying a layer of noodles on the bottom of a 9"x13" baking dish. Spoon over 1/2 the ricotta cheese mixture, then spoon over 1/2 the mozzarella cheese, then spread over 1/2 of the meat sauce. Repeat this step.

Bake at 375° for 30 minutes and let lasagna rest after taking it out of the oven for 10 minutes to firm up. Then slice and serve.

Recipe Tips

This recipe is ideal to make a day ahead for a family gathering and we've made it many many times. If you make it ahead refrigerate it and then allow an additional 15-20 minutes of cooking time.

Tuna Pasta Casserole

The breakfast every morning was so yummy and the dinning room had such a wonderful view of the bay. It was a really great way to start the day. – Guest

2	cups	elbow macaroni, uncooked
2 1/2	cups	water
2		chicken bouillon cubes
1/8	tsp	black pepper
1	tsp	fresh basil leaves
1	cup	frozen green beans
1	cup	milk
1/2	cup	cheddar cheese, grated
3/4	cup	tuna, canned and drained
1/4	cup	fresh parsley, chopped

Procedure

Bring water, bouillon cubes, pepper and basil leaves to a boil in a 4-quart pot. Gradually add pasta so that water continues to boil. Cover and simmer for 7 minutes, stirring occasionally. Add green beans and milk into pot; cover and simmer 6-8 minutes or until pasta and beans are tender. Stir in cheese, tuna, and parsley until cheese is melted. Serve immediately.

Tuna With Noodles

Our rooms were perfect for our stay – no detail was left out with regards to our comfort and enjoyment right down to a sweet little rubber ducky by the tub for our son. He certainly enjoyed his baths with his new friend. – Guest

1 1/2	cups	egg noodles, cooked and drained
1	Tbsp	butter or margarine
1	Tbsp	flour
1/8	tsp	dried dill
1	cup	Carnation milk
1/2	cup	water
1/2	tsp	instant chicken bouillon granules
2	cans	tuna, drained
1/2	cup	peas
1/3	cup	potato chips

Procedure

Preheat oven to 400°. Grease 1-quart casserole.

Melt butter in medium saucepan. Stir in flour and dill; gradually stir in evaporated milk, water and boullion. Cook over medium heat, stirring constantly, until mixture is thickened. Stir in pasta, tuna and peas. Spoon into prepared casserole. Sprinkle with chips.

Bake for 8-10 minutes or until chips are golden brown. Season with salt and ground black pepper.

Recipe Tips

When using spaghetti, keep in mind that 8 oz of uncooked pasta makes 4 cups cooked.

All-Star Pork Meatballs

We were welcomed by the staff upon our arrival with offers to help us bring in our gear (we had a 17-month-old with us). We were immediately impressed with the Inn – it was immaculately clean, very nicely decorated but yet homey and welcoming at the same time. – Guest

1	lb	pork, ground
1	Tbsp	onion flakes
3/4	cup	cornflakes, crushed
1/2	tsp	salt
1/8	tsp	black pepper, ground
1	egg	
1/4	cup	ketchup
3	Tbsp	brown sugar
1	tsp	dry mustard

Procedure

Heat oven to 375°. In a large bowl, combine ground pork, onion flakes, cornflakes, salt, pepper, and egg.

In a small bowl stir together ketchup, brown sugar and dry mustard.

Spoon 2 tablespoons of the ketchup mixture into the pork and mix well.

Spray muffin tin with vegetable cooking spray. Form 6 meatballs and place in muffin tin.

Coat the top of each meatball with the remaining ketchup mixture.

Bake for 30 minutes at 375° until nicely browned and glazed.

Balsamic Pork Chops

8		boneless pork chops, about 1/2″ thick
1 1/2	cups	balsamic dressing

Procedure

Place chops in large, resealable bag; pour vinaigrette dressing into bag. Seal bag and refrigerate for 2-24 hours.

Remove chops from marinade and pat dry. Discard remaining marinade. Grill chops directly over barbecue for about 8-10 minutes, turning once.

Barbecue Pulled Pork

One of my favourite memories was having glasses of wine with my friends while sitting at the dining room window overlooking the Bay, looking toward Dildo Island and being impressed with our waitress's napkin folding ability. This is a B&B that functions IN STYLE while providing the relaxing, carefree vacation that all of us yearn to experience. – Guest

1	lb	boneless pork tenderloin
1/2	tsp	pepper
1/4	tsp	red pepper flakes
1	Tbsp	canola oil
1	cup	onion, diced
2		garlic cloves, minced
1/2	cup	barbecue sauce
1/4	cup	ketchup
1/4	cup	water
1	tsp	vinegar

Procedure

Heat the oven to 350°. Sear the whole tenderloin on all sides in a hot, non-stick pan. Remove from the heat and season with the pepper and red pepper flakes.

Cover the tenderloin with foil and bake for 25 minutes. Heat the oil in a medium saucepan and sauté the onion and garlic for 5 minutes.

Add the barbecue sauce, ketchup, water, and vinegar. Simmer for 10 minutes. Shred the pork with 2 forks. Add the pulled pork to the sauce. Serve on buns.

Electric Frying Pan Pork Chop Dinner

I felt at home. It was clear that everyone enjoyed their work and enjoyed having us stay at their beautiful B&B. – Guest

4	cups	mushrooms, sliced
3	Tbsp	vegetable oil, divided
1	lb	pork tenderloin, cut in 2″ pieces
2		red bell peppers, seeded and diced
1		medium onion, cut in 1″ pieces
1/2	tsp	dried thyme leaves, crushed
1	tsp	salt
1/4	tsp	pepper
3/4	cup	dry white wine or apple juice
2	tsp	cornstarch

Procedure

In an electric frying pan, over medium heat, heat 2 tablespoons oil until hot. Add pork; cook, stirring frequently, until it loses its pink colour, 8-9 minutes; remove to plate and keep warm.

To the electric frying pan, add remaining 1 tablespoon oil; add peppers, onion and prepared mushrooms; cover and simmer until vegetables are tender, about 10 minutes.

In a small bowl, combine cornstarch, thyme, and the salt and pepper with 3/4 cup water; stir into mushroom mixture along with the wine. Cook uncovered, stirring often, until sauce is clear and slightly thickened, 3-4 minutes. Return pork to electric frying pan; heat only until hot.

Granny Smith Pork Chops

The warm and welcoming attitude of the owners and of everyone who worked at the B&B gave a glow to our visit throughout the time we spent. – Guest

4		large pork chops
2		Granny Smith apple, halved, cored and thinly sliced
2	tsp	butter
2	Tbsp	brown sugar

Procedure

Preheat your oven to 350°. Place the pork chops in a sprayed shallow baking dish and season with salt and pepper. Cover and bake at 350° for 30 minutes.

Uncover and place peeled, cored and sliced apples on top of the pork chops. Add little dabs of butter across the top of the dish and bake for an additional 15 minutes uncovered.

Honey Garlic Pork Chops

Todd recalls, "Many a day we'd come home from school and open the door and the smell of Mom making Honey-Grilled Pork Chops for dinner. We couldn't wait for Dad to get home so we could dig in."

4		boneless pork chops, about 1/2" thick
1/4	cup	lemon juice
1/4	cup	honey
2	Tbsp	soy sauce
1	Tbsp	dry sherry
2		cloves garlic, minced

Procedure

Combine all ingredients except pork chops in small bowl.

Place pork in shallow baking dish; pour marinade over pork. Cover and Refrigerate 4 hours or overnight. Remove pork from marinade. Heat remaining marinade in small saucepan over medium heat to simmer. Broil pork 4"-6" from heat source 12-15 minutes, turning once during cooking and basting frequently with marinade.

Sweet & Sour Pork

We enjoyed an immaculate room, a scrumptious-homemade-gourmet-full course meal (complete with a little *martini* humour) and a yummy breakfast to boot. – Guest

2	Tbsp	vegetable oil
2	lbs	lean pork, cut into strips
2 1/2	cups	chunked pineapple
1/4	cup	brown sugar
2	Tbsp	cornstarch
1/4	cup	vinegar
1	Tbsp	soy sauce
1/2	tsp	salt
3/4	cup	green pepper, seeded and thinly sliced into strips
1/4	cup	onions, thinly sliced
4	cups	chow mein noodles

Procedure

In a frying pan heat the vegetable oil and slowly brown the pork. Add 1/4 cup of water, cover the frying pan and simmer until the pork is tender, which should take about 1 hour.

Drain the pineapple and reserve the liquid for later use in the recipe. In a bowl combine the brown sugar and cornstarch, add the pineapple syrup, vinegar, soy sauce and salt. Pour into the frying pan over low heat and stir until sauce thickens.

Pour over the cooked pork and let sit for 10 minutes. Add the chunked pineapple, green pepper and onion and return the frying pan to the stove and cook over medium heat for 5 minutes. Serve over rice or noodles and top with chow mein noodles.

Sweet & Sour Spareribs

The hosts thought of everything (including warm, homemade cookies for the road!) and did their utmost to ensure that our visit represented the very best of Newfoundland. – Guest

4	lbs	spareribs
3	Tbsp	soy sauce
1/3	cup	prepared mustard
1	cup	brown sugar
1/2	tsp	garlic salt

Procedure

In a roasting pan place the spareribs and bake at 325° for 45 minutes and drain liquid after baking.

In a bowl, mix soy sauce, mustard, brown sugar, and garlic and then brush the mixture all over the ribs. Reduce the heat of the oven and return the ribs to the oven and bake for an additional 2 hours or until the ribs are done and tender. Baste with any remaining sauce from time to time while cooking and baste with pan drippings.

Roasted Pork

2	Tbsp	butter
1	cup	fresh sage
1 1/2	Tbsp	whole black peppercorns
2	tsp	cumin seeds
3	lbs	pork roast, tied with string
4		red onions, halved
3		bulbs fennel, untrimmed
2	Tbsp	olive oil
1 1/2	cups	orange juice
1/2	cup	chicken stock
1	Tbsp	balsamic vinegar
		salt to taste

Procedure

Melt butter in frying pan over medium high heat. Add 1/2 cup sage and stir until leaves are slightly darker green and crisp, about 1 minute. Transfer with slotted spoon to towels to drain. When leaves are cool, wrap in towels and seal in plastic bag. Save butter.

Finely grind peppercorns and cumin in a spice grinder. Rinse pork and pat dry; rub pepper mixture all over the meat. Tuck remaining sage leaves equally under the strings on the smooth (fattiest) side of the roast. Set the pork, herb side up, on a rack in a 10"x15" pan.

Cut onions in half crosswise; don't peel. Trim off feathery fennel tops and reserve. Trim any bruises or dark spots from fennel. Rinse, then slice each vertically to make 3 or 4 equal slices.

Pour 2 tablespoons olive oil into a 10"x12"x15" rimmed pan and tilt to coat. Turn onions cut side down in pan. Turn fennel slices in pan to coat with oil.

Put roast on middle rack in 400° oven. Drizzle fennel with 3/4 cup orange juice. Set vegetables on rack beneath pork. Bake until fennel slices are browned lightly on the bottom, about 35 minutes, then turn slices. Continue to cook with onions until both vegetables are browned on the bottom, about 20 minutes longer. If drippings in the pan get dark enough to scorch, pour a couple tablespoons of water onto them and tilt pan to distribute moisture. Bake pork about 45 minutes.

Transfer meat to large platter and keep warm; let stand at least 10 minutes. Add 2 tablespoons water to vegetables and tilt pan to distribute moisture; leave in pan and keep warm.

Remove rack and discard fat, then add reserved butter, remaining 3/4 cup orange juice, broth, and vinegar to roast pan. Boil on high heat, stirring to release browned drippings, until reduced to about 1/2 cup, about 10 minutes. Drain juices from pork into pan.

Arrange onions and fennel with pork. If desired, add some of the feathery greens from fennel tops. Sprinkle with the fried sage leaves. Slice roast and serve with vegetables and sauce. Add salt to taste.

40-Clove Chicken

The chicken is infused with the garlic and tastes excellent. The first time we saw this recipe was on Ina Garten's TV show and I just had to make it that day. Needless to say if you believe in vampires it'll keep them at bay.

6		chicken breasts, boneless and skinless
1	tsp	sea salt
1	tsp	pepper
1/4	cup	olive oil
40		cloves garlic, peeled
1/2	cup	fresh parsley, chopped

Procedure

Preheat oven to 400°.

Season chicken all over with salt and pepper. Drizzle with oil and arrange in a single layer in a 13"x9" baking dish. Scatter garlic cloves over chicken. Cover and bake 20 minutes.

Sprinkle with parsley and bake, uncovered, 10 minutes longer.

Recipe Tips

Microwave garlic cloves for 15 seconds and the skins slip right off.

Autumn Chicken Pot Pie

We can't say enough about the warm and gracious hospitality we experienced. – Guest

Dough

1	cup	all-purpose flour
1	tsp	ginger, ground
1	tsp	lemon zest, grated
1/2	tsp	salt
1/3	cup	butter, softened
3	Tbsp	cold water

Filling

2	cups	chicken, cooked and chopped
2	cups	chicken broth
1	cup	pearl onions, peeled and steamed until tender
2		medium carrots, cut into slices and steamed until tender
1		medium Granny Smith apples, cored and cut into chunks
1/4	cup	dried cranberries
2	Tbsp	butter
1/4	cup	flour
2	Tbsp	lemon juice
1	Tbsp	fresh ginger root, minced
1/2	tsp	black pepper, ground
1/8	tsp	salt

Procedure

In large bowl combine flour, ginger, lemon zest, and salt. With a pastry blender or 2 knives, cut in 1/3 cup butter until mixture resembles coarse crumbs. Sprinkle 3 tablespoons of water over the mixture and toss with fork. The dough should be just barely moistened, enough to hold together when formed into a ball. Add more water if needed. Form the dough into a flat disk and wrap in plastic. Refrigerate while making the filling.

Preheat oven to 450°.

Drop pearl onions into boiling water for 30 seconds; drain, peel. Steam pearl onions and carrots until tender.

In large saucepan over medium heat, melt 2 tablespoons butter. Whisk in flour and ginger until smooth. Reduce heat to low and gradually whisk in chicken broth. Stir in pearl onions, carrots, apples, cranberries, lemon juice and chicken. Let simmer for 5 minutes, stirring regularly. Season with salt and pepper. Spoon filling into deep, 10" ceramic or glass pie dish.

On a lightly floured surface, roll dough out to a circle, about 12" in diameter. Lay the dough over the top of pie dish. Trim and crimp edges. Use a small knife to cut several slits in the centre of pie. (Alternatively, make decorative cuts in pie crust before setting it on top of pie.) Set the pie on a baking sheet and place in oven on middle rack. Bake for 15 minutes. Reduce heat to 400° and continue baking for additional 20 minutes, until pie bubbles around edges and top is nicely browned. Serve while piping hot.

Baked Chicken and Rice

Very simple baked dish.

1	lb	boneless skinless chicken breasts
1		can cream of mushroom soup
1	cup	water
1		envelope onion soup mix
1	cup	rice, not instant rice

Procedure

Place chicken in prepared casserole dish.

In separate bowl mix together remaining ingredients. Pour over chicken.

Cover and bake at 375°. for 1 hour.

Recipe Tips

Chicken is easily skinned and boned if slightly frozen.

Chicken & Rice Dinner

This recipe is easily cooked in one skillet or French oven. I've used this recipe as a base to create lots of other dishes by adding different canned soups. It is a take-off version of Andres' Arroz Con Pollo.

1	Tbsp	vegetable oil
4		boneless, skinless chicken breasts
1	can	chicken soup
1 1/3	cups	milk
1 1/2	cups	quick-cooking rice, uncooked
		salt and pepper to taste

Procedure

Heat oil in a large non-stick pan over medium-high heat. Add chicken; cover. Cook 4 minutes on each side or until cooked thoroughly.

Remove chicken from pan. Add soup and water; stir to mix and bring to a boil. Stir in rice, then top with chicken; cover. Reduce heat to low and cook 5 minutes.

Recipe Tips

Burned a pot of rice? Just place a piece of white bread on top of the rice for 5-10 minutes to draw out the burned flavour. Be careful not to scrape the burned pieces off of the bottom of the pan when serving the rice.

Chicken Bacon Roll-Ups

Owners very friendly and informative. Common areas perfect for relaxing. One of the two or three best B&Bs we have visited, and would go again.
– Guest

16	slices	bacon
8		chicken thighs, skins removed

Marinade

1		orange rind, grated, and juice
5		cloves garlic, crushed
1	Tbsp	chili powder
1	Tbsp	paprika
1	tsp	cumin, ground
1/2	tsp	oregano, dried
1	Tbsp	olive oil

Procedure

Start with the marinade by combining citrus rind, juice, garlic, chili powder, paprika, cumin, oregano, and olive oil in a bowl.

Roll up each chicken thigh with 2 strips of bacon in a criss-cross pattern. Secure with toothpicks or skewers. Arrange roll-ups in an ovenproof glass dish.

Pour the marinade over the roll-ups, cover and marinade at room temperature for 1 hour or overnight in the refrigerator.

Preheat the oven to 375° and put the dish in the oven. Bake for 40 minutes to 1 hour, depending on the size of the thighs.

Recipe Tips

Don't use white chicken meat for this recipe as it will be too dry and besides thighs are inexpensive and makes this a very family-friendly meal.

Chicken Cordon Bleu

Beautifully restored heritage house, with excellent, firm bed, wonderful bathroom with two person jetted tub, very quiet room and lovely view of bay, coastline and townsite. Very good breakfast. – Guest

8		boneless skinless chicken breasts
8		ham slices
8		Swiss cheese slices
3	Tbsp	parsley, chopped
1/4	tsp	pepper
2		eggs, beaten
1	cup	Italian bread crumbs
1/4	cup	butter or margarine
1	can	can of cream of mushroom soup
1	cup	sour cream

Procedure

Start by preheating your oven to 350°. Rinse the chicken breasts and pat dry with paper towels. Pound the chicken breasts to 1/4" thick with a meat mallet.

Top each fillet with a slice of ham, then top with a slice of cheese, and in a separate bowl mix the parsley and pepper and then sprinkle it evenly over the chicken fillets.

Roll the chicken fillets to enclose the filling and secure with toothpicks or skewers. Dip the rolls in the eggs and then roll them in the bread crumbs.

In a large frying pan melt the butter and brown the rolls in the butter. Place the rolls in a 9"x13" baking dish. Stir the soup and sour cream into any of the drippings left in the frying pan. Pour this mixture over the chicken rolls.

Bake for 45 minutes.

Chicken Parmigiana

The meals were delicious and prepared with a lot of extra thought and personal touch. There was a family atmosphere, both quiet and cozy. The staff was friendly and discreet. – Guest

2		eggs
1	tsp	salt
1/8	tsp	pepper
6		chicken breast fillets
3/4	cup	crackers, crushed
1/2	cup	vegetable oil
15	oz	tomato sauce
1/4	tsp	basil
1/8	tsp	garlic powder
1	Tbsp	butter
1/2	cup	Parmesan cheese, grated
8	oz	mozzarella cheese slices, cut into triangles

Procedure

Begin by preheating your oven to 350°. Beat the eggs with salt and pepper in a small bowl. Rinse the chicken breasts and pat dry with paper towels. Dip the chicken breasts into the egg mixture and then roll them in the cracker crumbs, ensuring to coat them well.

In a frying pan add the oil and brown the coated chicken breasts, remove the chicken breasts and drain any excess fat by putting them on paper towels.

Put the chicken in 9"x13" baking dish. In the frying pan add the tomato sauce, basil and garlic powder to a boil. Simmer for 10 minutes and the sauce will thicken slightly.

Pour the sauce over the chicken and sprinkle with Parmesan cheese and bake covered in a 350° oven for 30 minutes.

Remove from the oven and arrange the mozzarella slices over the top of each of the breasts and return to the oven uncovered for an additional 10 minutes of baking.

Recipe Tips

Marinate chicken in buttermilk to tenderize.

Chicken Piccata

I spent 3 weeks at Inn By The Bay in August and it far surpassed my expectations! My room was immaculate and so comfortable and homey. – Guest

2		chicken breasts, boneless, skinless
2	Tbsp	olive oil
1/4	cup	dry white wine
1	tsp	garlic, minced
1/2	cup	chicken broth
2	Tbsp	fresh lemon juice
1	Tbsp	capers, drained
2	Tbsp	butter
2		lemons, sliced
2	Tbsp	parsley, chopped

Procedure

Take the chicken breasts and split them in half and then pound them to 1/4" thick. Pat dry with paper towels.

In a bowl mix the salt, pepper and flour. Dredge the cutlets in the salt, pepper and flour mixture and shake off any excess mixture.

Spray a frying pan and heat the olive oil on medium heat. Sauté cutlets for 3 minutes on one side and then turn over and fry an additional 3 minutes on the other side. Take the cutlets out of the pan and put on a plate layered with paper towels.

Deglaze the pan with the wine and then add the garlic and brown the garlic until lightly golden brown. Add the chicken broth and lemon juice and capers and bring to a light boil.

Return the cutlets to the pan and cook 1 minute per side and then remove to a platter. Add butter and lemon slices to the pan and once the butter is melted give the mixture a quick whisk and then pour over the cutlets. Garnish with chopped parsley.

Chicken Range Cacciatore

I LOVE this place. We stayed there only one night but we enjoyed every second of it. We booked it a couple weeks before our trip, and they had this great room in George House with the bay view. I was nicely surprised with the quality of services there. – Guest

1		whole chicken, cut up into pieces
1	Tbsp	oil
1		onion, sliced
1	can	stewed tomatoes (approx 14-oz can)
2	Tbsp	brown sugar (firmly packed)
1		package spaghetti sauce mix

Procedure

Heat a large, deep frying pan over medium-high heat. Add oil and heat until hot. Cook chicken until golden brown on all sides, about 5 minutes. Add onion and sauté until softened, about 3 more minutes.

Stir tomatoes (undrained), sugar and spaghetti sauce mix into skillet with chicken and onions. Bring mixture to a boil, cover and reduce heat. Gently simmer until chicken is done, about 30 minutes. Serve warm.

Crock-Pot Orange Chicken

We were welcomed in and treated like family but like the favourite child or aunt. Todd, Dale and staff were friendly, took time to listen to our stories, shared theirs and were always glad to see us when we returned from day trips. – Guest

6		chicken breasts, boneless, skinless
1/2	tsp	ginger
1	tsp	salt
		pepper to taste
1	cup	frozen orange juice from concentrate
1 1/2	cups	coconut, shredded
2	cups	orange segments or mandarin oranges from a can
2		green onion, chopped

Procedure

Put chicken, ginger, salt, pepper, and frozen orange juice in Crock-Pot and cook on low 6 hours. Serve chicken on hot cooked rice on platter. Top with coconut, orange segments and green onions. Serve chicken liquid in gravy boat, if desired.

Crispy Chicken Bake

Bel accueil, très belle maison et service compétent. – Guest

1/2	cup	flour
1/4	tsp	pepper
2		eggs
2	Tbsp	water
1	cup	rice crispies, crushed
1	cup	Parmesan cheese, grated
1		package dry onion soup mix
6		chicken breasts, boneless, skinless
1/4	cup	butter or margarine, melted

Procedure

Preheat oven to 375°. Coat a 13"x9"x2" baking pan with vegetable cooking spray.

In a shallow dish combine flour and pepper.

Beat eggs and water in a small bowl.

Combine rice cereal, Parmesan cheese, and onion soup mix in a bowl.

Dredge chicken in flour mixture, followed by a dip in the eggs. Roll in cereal until evenly coated. Arrange in a single layer in prepared baking dish and drizzle with melted butter. Bake, uncovered, for 30 minutes or until done. Serve warm.

Recipe Tips

To reuse cooking oil without tasting whatever was cooked in the oil previously, cook a 1/3 piece of ginger in the oil. It will remove any remaining flavours and odours.

Fried Chicken

Comfortable room, wonderful breakfast and dinner. Very attentive host and service folks. – Guest

1 1/4	cups	flour
1	tsp	salt
1	tsp	baking powder
1/2	tsp	dried thyme
1/4	tsp	black pepper, ground
1		egg
3/4	cup	milk
1/2	cup	vegetable oil, divided
9		chicken pieces (legs, wings, thighs, ribs, and centre breast)

Procedure

Combine flour, salt, baking powder, thyme and pepper in a medium-sized mixing bowl; set aside.

Beat egg in a small bowl until frothy. Add milk and 2 tablespoons oil; beat until well blended. Pour into flour mixture; stir until well blended.

Heat remaining 6 tablespoons oil over medium heat in a large skillet. Dip chicken pieces in batter; shake off any excess. Fry chicken for about 10 minutes, turning until lightly browned all over.

Lower heat to very low, cover tightly and simmer for about 30 minutes. Turn pieces periodically to ensure even cooking; add 1-2 tablespoons water during cooking if pan becomes too dry. Uncover during final 4-5 minutes to allow skin to become crisp. Serve hot or cold.

Marjorie's Chicken Rolls Supreme

This recipe was given to Todd by Marjorie Baetzel. She made this dish once when Todd visited her house for dinner and it was delicious. We like making this as it is easy to make and enjoyed by all. I recommend serving it with garlic mashed potatoes and glazed carrots.

6		boneless skinless chicken breasts
2 1/2	cups	bread crumbs
1/4	cup	Parmesan cheese
1	tsp	salt
2	tsp	parsley flakes
3/4	cup	butter, melted
1/4	tsp	garlic powder
1	tsp	mustard
1	tsp	Worcestershire sauce

Procedure

Put the melted butter in a pie plate. In a bowl mix the bread crumbs, Parmesan cheese, parsley flakes, garlic powder, mustard, and Worcestershire sauce and put into a second pie plate. Dredge the chicken breasts through the butter mixture one at a time and then coat well in the bread crumb mixture.

Roll the chicken breasts and place open side down on a glass baking dish. Pour remaining butter over the rolls and cover with aluminum foil and bake in a 325° oven for 50-55 minutes – no longer.

You can check on the dish throughout the baking process and baste the chicken breasts with the pan drippings.

Recipe Tips

Don't throw out all that leftover wine: Freeze into ice cubes for future use in casseroles and sauces.

Parmesan Chicken Thighs

Lovely scenic and quiet location with comfortable room and excellent cuisine. – Guest

1	cup	mayonnaise
1	cup	Parmesan cheese, grated
1	tsp	Italian seasoning
2	lbs	chicken thighs, boneless, skinless
1/4	tsp	salt
1/8	tsp	black pepper

Procedure

Preheat oven to 400°.

In a small bowl combine mayonnaise, Parmesan cheese, and Italian seasoning.

Season chicken on both sides with salt and pepper and place in a single layer in a 8" square baking dish.

Generously spread with sauce and bake for 20 minutes, or until done. Serve warm.

Recipe Tips

When mincing garlic, sprinkle on a little salt so the pieces won't stick to your knife or cutting board.

Spicy Baked Chicken

Great food, grand rooms, with good friends and a terrific view. – Guest

2		fresh chickens, cut into pieces
1	cup	bread crumbs
1/2	tsp	onion powder
1/2	tsp	garlic powder
1/4	tsp	cayenne pepper
1/8	tsp	ginger, ground
1/3	cup	plain yogourt

Procedure

Preheat oven to 350°. Lightly spray a medium baking dish with vegetable cooking spray; set aside.

Rinse chicken pieces and pat dry.

In a shallow bowl, combine bread crumbs, onion powder, garlic powder, cayenne pepper and ginger. Dip chicken pieces in yogourt, then into crumb mixture. Place in prepared dish. Bake, uncovered, for 45-50 minutes or until chicken is tender.

Stuffed Cranberry And Rice Chicken

Every staff member: Todd, Tammy, Dale etc were fantastic and treated us wonderfully. – Guest

6		boneless skinless chicken breasts, pounded to 1/2″ thick
3	cups	brown rice, cooked
1/2	cup	dried cranberries, rehydrated and drained
1	Tbsp	olive oil
1/2	cup	celery, diced
1/2	cup	onion, diced
2	tsp	fresh thyme, minced
1	cup	dry white wine

Procedure

Prepare the chicken breasts and set aside. Combine the rice and rehydrated cranberries and mix well. Set aside.

Heat the oil in a small saucepan over medium-high heat. Add the celery and onion and sauté for 5 minutes. Add the vegetables and thyme to the rice.

On a flat surface, take about 1/2 cup of the rice mixture and place on the lower third of each chicken breast. Fold over the sides of the chicken breast and roll up. Secure each breast with a toothpick. Continue with all chicken breasts.

Place all the chicken rolls in a casserole dish. Pour wine in the bottom of the dish. Cover and bake in a preheated 350° oven for 20 minutes. Uncover and bake for 10 more minutes.

Pepsi Cola Chicken

Friendly and helpful staff. Extremely clean and comfortable rooms. Good food and lovely setting. – Guest

6		boneless skinless chicken breasts
1	cup	ketchup
1	cup	Pepsi Cola
2	Tbsp	Worcestershire sauce

Procedure

In a 9"x13" casserole dish place the chicken and sprinkle with salt and pepper. In a bowl mix the ketchup, cola, and Worcestershire sauce and pour over the chicken. Cover and bake in a 350° oven for 50 minutes.

Weekend Chicken & Dumplings

Purely pleasure. Sophomoric humour at a place called "Dildo." (blush)
– Guest

Chicken Recipe

1	cup	potatoes, peeled and cut into 1/2" cubes
1/2	cup	carrots, peeled and diced
1/4	cup	celery, finely chopped
1/4	cup	onion, finely chopped
1	cup	chicken, chopped
		water
		salt and pepper to taste

Dumplings

1 1/2	cups	flour
1/3	cup	butter, softened
1	tsp	salt
2	tsp	baking powder
2	tsp	white sugar
		milk

Procedure

For the chicken recipe put vegetables in a large pot and cove with water and boil the vegetables until soft. Add the chopped chicken and ensure all ingredients in the pot are covered with water; add salt and pepper and heat to boiling. Boil until the chicken is fully cooked.

In a bowl combine the flour, butter, salt, baking powder, and sugar. Add enough milk to make a stiff dough. Drop the dumplings by the spoonfuls into the boiling chicken mixture in the pot. Cover the pot and reduce heat for 20 minutes without lifting the lid.

Wild Chicken Casserole

Informal but deeply gracious hospitality. We felt welcome, cared for, and in the hands of true professionals. – Guest

1/2	cup	wild rice, uncooked
1/2	tsp	salt
1 1/2	cups	water
1 1/2	tsp	butter
1	cup	mushrooms, sliced
1/4	cup	chicken broth
1 1/3	cups	chicken, cooked and chopped
1/4	tsp	pepper
1	can	cream of chicken soup
1/2	can	milk (measure with soup can)
2/3	cup	cheese, shredded

Procedure

Begin by cooking the wild rice in salted water in a pot for 45 minutes or until all of the water is absorbed by the rice.

Preheat the oven to 325°. Add butter, mushrooms, chicken broth, chicken and pepper to rice mixture. Heat the soup, milk and cheese in a separate pot, stirring the mixture until smooth.

Add the soup mixture to the rice mixture and then spoon into a sprayed 2-quart baking dish and bake for 1 hour at a 325° oven.

George HOUSE

HERITAGE BED & BREAKFAST

SAUCES

Aunt Mary's Bologna Gravy

Todd recalls his Aunt Mary serving this bologna gravy when he was a child and she would serve it with french fries.

2	Tbsp	butter (no substitutes)
2	Tbsp	flour
2	cups	milk
1/2	tsp	salt
		Tabasco sauce to taste (few drops)
1/2	tsp	Worcestershire sauce
2	cups	bologna, ground

Procedure

Melt the butter and blend in the flour making a roux. Gradually stir in the milk bringing it to a boil. Stirring and cook until thickened. Season with salt, Tabasco and Worcestershire sauce. Stir in the bologna and serve hot.

Chicken Pan Gravy

1/4	cup	pan drippings from roast chicken
1/4	cup	flour
1 1/2	cups	chicken broth or apple juice

Procedure

After transferring roast chicken to a serving platter, pour pan drippings into a large measuring cup. Skim and reserve fat from drippings.

Pour 1/4 cup of the fat into a medium saucepan (discard remaining fat). Stir in flour. Add enough broth or water to remaining drippings in the measuring cup to equal 2 cups; add all at once to flour mixture in saucepan. Cook and stir over medium heat until thick and bubbly. Cook and stir for 1 minute more. Season to taste with salt and pepper. Makes 2 cups (8-10 servings).

Recipe Tips

If you are making gravy and accidentally burn it, just pour it into a clean pan and continue cooking it. Add sugar a little at a time, tasting as you go to avoid over-sugaring it. The sugar will cancel out the burned taste.

Quick Brown Sauce

Serve with meats or other dishes or use as base for Bordelaise sauce.

3	Tbsp	butter
3	Tbsp	flour
1 1/2	cups	soup stock or vegetable stock
1/2	tsp	thyme
		sprig parsley
		salt
		pepper, freshly ground

Procedure

Melt the butter in a heavy saucepan over low heat. Add flour and blend well over medium heat. Reduce heat and simmer for several minutes.

Heat bouillon or stock, stir into the roux (flour and butter mixture) and continue stirring until sauce thickens.

Add herbs, reduce heat and simmer for several minutes.

Savoury Turkey Gravy

5	cups	turkey stock
1/4	cup	flour
1	cup	water
1	tsp	poultry seasoning
1	tsp	salt
1/2	tsp	pepper
1/4	tsp	celery salt

Procedure

In a medium saucepan, bring the turkey stock to a boil. In a small bowl, dissolve flour in water. Gradually whisk into the turkey stock. Season with poultry seasoning, salt, pepper, and celery salt. Bring to a boil, reduce heat, and simmer for 8-10 minutes, or until thickened.

Recipe Tips

Brown gravy in a hurry with a bit of instant coffee straight from the jar . . . no bitter taste, either.

Todd's Big Turkey Gravy

1		neck, heart, gizzard from turkey giblets
1		medium carrot, thickly sliced
1		medium onion, thickly sliced
1		celery stalk, thickly sliced
1/2	tsp	salt
1		turkey liver
3	Tbsp	fat from poultry drippings
3	Tbsp	flour
1/2	tsp	salt
1/3	cup	red wine or sherry
		salt and pepper to taste

Procedure

In a 3-quart saucepan, over high heat, place neck, heart, gizzard, vegetables, and salt in enough water to cover. Heat to boiling. Reduce heat to low; cover and simmer 45 minutes.

Add liver and cook 15 minutes longer. Strain broth into a large bowl; cover and reserve broth in the refrigerator.

To make the gravy, remove the cooked turkey and roasting rack from the roasting pan. Pour poultry drippings through a sieve into a 4-cup measuring cup.

Add 1 cup giblet broth to the roasting pan and stir until the crusty brown bits are loosened; pour the deglazed liquid/broth into the 4-cup measure. Let the mixture stand a few minutes, until the fat rises to the top.

Over medium heat, spoon 3 tablespoons fat from the poultry drippings into a 2-quart saucepan. Whisk flour and salt into the heated fat and continue to cook and stir until the flour turns golden.

Meanwhile, skim and discard any fat that remains on top of the poultry drippings. Add remaining broth and enough water to the poultry drippings to equal 3 1/2 cups.

Gradually whisk in warm poultry drippings/broth mixture.

Add red wine or sherry. Season with salt and pepper and heat to the simmering point. Serve hot in a warm gravy boat.

Recipe Tips

You can correct greasy gravy by adding a little baking soda to it.

SAUCES SAUCES SAUCES

Basic White Sauce

Dale recalls, "My mom made this many times and as a kid I hated it. She would serve creamed peas on toast using this recipe, or even sliced carrots, boiled and then smothered in this white sauce. Now, years later and a bit more mature, I love this recipe, and while I'm still not keen on 'creamed peas on toast,' I do like this basic white sauce on light fish fillets, over carrots or other root vegetables."

2	cups	milk
2	Tbsp	butter
1/4	cup	white flour
		salt and pepper to taste

Procedure

In a saucepan warm the milk being careful not to boil the milk. In a separate saucepan melt the butter and stir in the four and cook the roux gently over low heat for 2-3 minutes all the while, ensuring that the mixture does not brown.

Remove the saucepan from the heat and gradually add the milk mixture, stirring continuously and incorporating to make a smooth sauce.

Return to heat and bring to a boil slowly, again stirring constantly. Simmer for an additional 3-4 minutes until the sauce thickens. Season with salt and pepper.

Beginner Hollandaise Sauce

1	cup	mayonnaise
2		egg whites
2	Tbsp	lemon juice
1/2	tsp	dry mustard
1/4	tsp	salt

Procedure

In small saucepan, with a wire whisk, beat mayonnaise, egg whites, lemon juice, dry mustard, and salt until smooth. Stirring constantly, cook over medium-low heat until thick, but do not boil.

Basting Sauce

1	Tbsp	honey
1	Tbsp	Dijon mustard
1	Tbsp	soy sauce
1		clove garlic, minced

Procedure

In a small bowl, stir together ingredients.

Bechamel Sauce

1		small onion, chopped
1		small carrot, finely chopped
1		celery stalk, diced

Bouquet Garni

6		black peppercorns
	pinch	nutmeg, grated
1 1/4	cups	milk
2	Tbsp	butter
1/4	cup	white flour
2	Tbsp	cream
		salt and pepper to taste

Bouquet Garni

Bouquet garni is a collection of herbs (traditionally fresh parsley, fresh or dried thyme, and bay leaf) that are bundled together and cast adrift in your pot to flavour a soup, stew, or broth. They are tied together so they can be removed easily at the end of the cooking.

Procedure

In a saucepan put the onion, carrot, celery, bouquet garni, peppercorns, and milk. Bring to a boil and then remove from heat. Over low heat melt butter in a frying pan, remove from the heat and stir in the flour. Return frying pan to heat and cook the roux mixture for 2 minutes. Reheat the mixture in the saucepan until almost boiling. Strain mixture through a strainer into an extra large measuring cup. Ensure you get all the juices by pressing the vegetables into the strainer to extract any leftover juice. Add the saucepan mixture to the roux in the frying pan gradually, stirring constantly until the mixture is smooth. Return the frying pan to the stove and cook gently until the sauce thickens, ensuring to stir constantly. Simmer the sauce for 4-5 minutes. Remove the pan from the heat and season with salt and pepper to taste and then finish by stirring in the cream.

Bernaise Sauce

3	Tbsp	white wine vinegar
2	Tbsp	water
1		small onion, finely chopped
		tarragon
1		bay leaf
6		black peppercorns, crushed
1/2	cup	butter
2		egg yolks
1	Tbsp	herbs (tarragon, parsley, chervil), chopped

Procedure

In a saucepan add the vinegar, water, onion, tarragon, bay left and peppercorns. Simmer gently until the mixture reduces by half. Strain the mixture and cool in a bowl.

In another bowl cream the butter until soft. Place the bowl over a saucepan of simmering water similar to a double boiler, whisk in the egg yolks and liquid until everything is incorporated and fluffy in texture. Ensure that the water does not boil in the saucepan or the egg mixture will cook and the sauce will curdle. Gradually add the butter 1 teaspoon at a time and whisk it into the mixture. Continue to do so until all of the butter is gone. Add the tablespoon of fresh herbs and stir. Serve this sauce warm, not hot, with a grilled steak or freshly steamed or boiled vegetables.

Recipe Tips

This sauce is excellent and can be changed into another great sauce by adding 1 tablespoon of tomato paste at the beginning of the recipe and then using the sauce with lamb, or roast meat.

Béarnaise Sauce

1/2	cup	white wine
1	Tbsp	shallots or scallions, finely chopped
1/2	tsp	fresh tarragon (to taste), chopped
4		egg yolks
1/2	tsp	salt
1/2	cup	butter

Procedure

Combine wine, shallots and tarragon, and cook until wine is reduced to a mere glaze. Combine egg yolks and salt in blender.

Slowly pour glaze in blender, blending as it is poured. Heat butter until bubbling hot. Turn on blender again and gradually pour melted butter in steady stream until sauce thickens.

Berry Blueberry Chutney

4	cups	frozen or fresh blueberries
1	can	whole berry cranberry sauce (approx 16 oz)
1/4	cup	sugar
3	Tbsp	balsamic vinegar
1 1/2	tsp	orange peel, grated
1	tsp	ginger, ground
1/4-1/2	tsp	red pepper, crushed
1/4	tsp	pepper

Procedure

In a medium non-reactive saucepan combine blueberries, cranberry sauce, sugar, balsamic vinegar, orange peel, ginger, and red and black peppers. Bring to a boil; boil uncovered, stirring frequently, until slightly thickened, 15-20 minutes.

Blender Hollandaise Sauce

1/4	lb	butter
3		egg yolks
1	Tbsp	lemon juice
1	Tbsp	sherry
3	dashes	cayenne pepper

Procedure

Melt butter to low boiling point. Place all other ingredients in blender and blend at low speed until mixed.

Slowly pour in melted butter and blend 10 seconds or until thick and creamy.

Cheese Sauce

1	Tbsp	butter
1/2	Tbsp	flour
		salt
		pepper to taste
	pinch	cayenne pepper
1	cup	milk
1		egg yolk
1	Tbsp	Parmesan cheese

Procedure

Melt the butter in a small saucepan and stir in the flour and seasonings to taste. Add the milk. Stir continuously until sauce thickens.

Remove pan from heat and stir in the egg yolk. Stir in the cheese.

Easy Barbecue Sauce

1	cup	tomato sauce
3	Tbsp	Worcestershire sauce
1/2	cup	vegetable oil
1/4	cup	cider vinegar
3	tsp	dry mustard
3	Tbsp	brown sugar
2	tsp	chili powder
2	tsp	sugar
1/2	tsp	garlic powder
2	Tbsp	dried onion, minced
1/2	tsp	salt
1/4	tsp	black pepper

Procedure

Blend cornstarch and bourbon until smooth. Combine with all remaining ingredients in a small saucepan. Cook and stir over moderate heat until sauce boils; reduce heat and simmer 10 minutes.

Cod Horseradish Sauce

2	Tbsp	butter
1/4	cup	flour
2/3	cup	milk
2/3	cup	fish stock
		salt and freshly ground black pepper
2	Tbsp	tomato paste
2	Tbsp	horseradish
2/3	cup	sour cream

Procedure

In a frying pan melt the butter and then stir in the flour and cook for 3-4 minutes creating a roux. Ensure to continue stirring so the roux does not brown.

Gradually whisk in the milk and fish stock into the roux. Season with salt and pepper to taste. Bring the sauce to a boil, stirring and then simmer for 3 more minutes again, still stirring the mixture, ensuring the sauce is smooth and thickened.

Blend the tomato paste and horseradish sauce with the sour cream in a separate saucepan. Bring the sauce to a boil while continuously stirring to ensure it doesn't burn. Reduce heat and simmer for 1 minute. Add the horseradish sauce to the thickened sauce and serve with fish.

Creamy Mustard Sauce

1/4	cup	grainy mustard
1/4	cup	sour cream
1/4	cup	mayonnaise
1	Tbsp	dried chives
1	tsp	lemon juice

Procedure

In small bowl combine mustard, sour cream, mayonnaise, chives and juice. Cover and chill at least 1 hour.

Dill Sauce

1 1/4	cups	dill pickle spears, finely chopped
1/2	cup	sour cream
1	Tbsp	prepared mustard
1/8	tsp	pepper

Procedure

In food processor, fitted with metal blade, or in blender, process pickle, sour cream, mustard and pepper until smooth.

Cover and chill at least 1 hour.

Hollandaise Sauce

3		egg yolks
1/4	cup	water
2	Tbsp	lemon juice
1/2	cup	cold butter, cut into 8 pieces
1/8	tsp	paprika
1/8	tsp	cayenne pepper

Procedure

Prepare hollandaise sauce by heating egg yolks, water and lemon juice in a small saucepan. Cook over very low heat, stirring constantly, until yolk mixture begins to bubble at edges.

Whisk in butter, 1 piece at a time, until melted and sauce is thickened. Stir in paprika and cayenne pepper. Season with salt to taste.

Remove from heat.

Recipe Tips

If Hollandaise curdles gradually beat 1 well-beaten egg yolk into the mixture.

Honey Herb Sauce

1/4	cup	honey
2	Tbsp	onion, minced
1/4	cup	butter
1/2	tsp	thyme, crushed
		salt and pepper to taste

Procedure

Combine all ingredients in a small saucepan and bring to a boil; cook 2 minutes.

Recipe Tips

If honey turns to sugar in your bottle, simply stand the bottle in hot water for a bit and watch the results.

Honey Mustard Sauce

1/4	cup	Dijon-style mustard
1	tsp	dried tarragon, crushed
1/4	cup	honey
2	Tbsp	white wine vinegar
2	tsp	olive oil
1	dash	salt
1	dash	pepper

Procedure

Combine mustard and tarragon; mix well.
Gradually blend in honey; add vinegar and oil; mix well.
Salt and pepper to taste.

Lemon Tartar Sauce

1/2	cup	mayonnaise
2	Tbsp	dill pickle, finely chopped
2	Tbsp	green onion, finely chopped
1	Tbsp	lemon peel, freshly grated
2	tsp	lemon juice, freshly squeezed

Procedure

In a small bowl, combine all ingredients.
Keep covered in refrigerator at least 4-6 hours before serving.

King's Crown Royal Sauce

Don't fret about using your Crown Royal for this recipe – it is only 5 tablespoons, after all – and you can always pour yourself a drink after dinner. This is a great sauce served with Atlantic or Pacific salmon.

1/4	cup	butter
5	Tbsp	Crown Royal
2/3	cup	double cream
		juice of 1/2 a lemon
		salt and pepper to taste

Procedure

In a frying pan add melted butter over medium heat until melted. Pour in the whisky and ignite it and wait until the flames die down. Pour the cream into the pan and bring to a boil, stirring constantly. Simmer until reduced and sauce slightly thickens. Add the lemon juice at the last minute of cooking.

Honey Sweet and Sour Sauce

1/2	cup	ketchup
1/4	cup	honey
2	Tbsp	lemon juice
1	tsp	cornstarch
1/2	tsp	garlic salt

Procedure

Combine all ingredients; cook and stir over medium heat 2-3 minutes or until mixture boils and thickens.

Maple Barbecue Sauce

This sauce is excellent on beef, pork or poultry.

3/4	cup	maple syrup
2	Tbsp	chili sauce
2	Tbsp	cider vinegar
1 1/2	Tbsp	onions, chopped
1	Tbsp	Worcestershire sauce
1	tsp	salt
1/2	tsp	dry mustard
1/2	tsp	pepper

Procedure

Combine all ingredients and brush on top of any meat you wish to barbecue.

Mornay Sauce

3		egg yolks, slightly whisked
1/4	cup	whipped cream
1	cup	Bechemel sauce, hot
1	tsp	white wine, tarragon vinegar, or lemon juice
1/4	cup	Parmesan cheese, grated

Procedure

Mix the egg yolks with the cream in a saucepan.

Add the Bechamel and simmer. Stir until boil.

Remove from heat and add the cheese. Stir well.

Mustard and Lemon Sauce

1/3	cup	butter
1 1/4	oz	chicken stock
3	Tbsp	flour
3		egg yolks
2	Tbsp	lemon juice
2	Tbsp	Dijon mustard
		pinch of cayenne
		salt to taste

Procedure

In a medium saucepan melt the butter. Add the flour. Cook for 3 minutes. Stir constantly.

Pour the broth. Simmer from 5-6 minutes. Stir constantly. Remove from heat and slightly whisk the egg yolks.

Add the lemon juice and mustard and stir well; put the saucepan on heat and let cook for 2 minutes. Add cayenne to taste.

Paul's Spaghetti Sauce

3/4	cup	onion, chopped
1		clove garlic, minced
3	Tbsp	olive oil
4	cups	stewed tomatoes, undrained
1 1/3	cups	tomato paste
1	cup	water
1	Tbsp	sugar
1 1/2	tsp	salt
1/2	tsp	pepper
1 1/2	tsp	oregano leaves, crushed
1		bay leaf

Procedure

In pot sauté onion and garlic in oil until tender but not browned. Stir in all ingredients. Simmer uncovered for 30 minutes.

Remove bay leaf. Enjoy.

Peppercorn Sauce

1	Tbsp	butter
2-3		shallots, coarsely chopped
1	Tbsp	brandy
4	Tbsp	dry white wine
6	Tbsp	chicken stock
1/2	cup	whipping cream
2-3	Tbsp	green peppercorns
2	Tbsp	vegetable oil

Procedure

In a frying pan melt the butter and then add the shallots and cook them for 2-3 minutes or until completely softened. Pour in the brandy, white wine and chicken stock. Bring to a boil and reduce by two-thirds, making sure to stir continuously.

Reduce the heat and add the cream and half of the peppercorns. Using your spoon that you are stirring the sauce with, gently break up the peppercorns against the side of the pan. Cook sauce gently for an additional 4 or 5 minutes until the sauce thickens.

Strain the sauce into a saucepan. Stir in the remaining 1/2 of the peppercorns. Keep the sauce warm and serve warm, not hot, ensuring not to burn the sauce.

Ramped-Up Barbecue Sauce

1/3	cup	Crown Royal
1	tsp	cornstarch
2/3	cup	orange juice
1	Tbsp	orange rind, grated
3	Tbsp	molasses
1	cup	barbecue sauce (for Easy Barbecue Sauce see page 184)

Pesto Sauce

2/3	cup	olive oil
2	cups	fresh parsley (tightly packed)
1/2	cup	Parmesan cheese, grated
2		cloves garlic
4	tsp	dried basil
1	Tbsp	capers, drained
1/8	tsp	pepper

Procedure

In a blender container or food processor bowl fitted with metal blade, combine olive oil, parsley, cheese, garlic, basil, capers, and pepper. Blend or process for 30 seconds or until mixture is smooth. Store in covered container and refrigerate.

Recipe Tips

Never heat pesto sauce – the basil will turn black and taste bitter.

Tarragon Cream Sauce

2	Tbsp	butter
1/2	tsp	dried tarragon
1		large shallot, finely chopped
1/8	cup	dry white wine
1/2	Tbsp	flour
1/2	cup	cream
1/2	cup	milk
1	Tbsp	parsley, finely chopped

Procedure

Melt butter in a small saucepan until butter begins to turn hazelnut brown. Add the tarragon and shallots and sauté until the shallots are tender.

Add the wine and simmer for 5-10 minutes. Then stir in the flour; add cream and milk and cook until thickened. Stir in parsley; serve.

Wino's Sauce

This sauce is good for chicken, fish or egg dishes.

6	Tbsp	butter
6	Tbsp	flour
1	cup	chicken broth
1	cup	heavy cream
1	Tbsp	sherry or dry white wine
1	tsp	white pepper

Procedure

Melt butter. Remove from heat, blend in flour and return to heat. Stir and cook a few minutes. Gradually stir in broth and simmer, stirring constantly until thick.

Gradually blend in cream, then sherry or wine. Season to taste. Serve immediately.

George HOUSE

HERITAGE BED & BREAKFAST

TIMELESS NEWFOUNDLAND FAVOURITES

Aunty Emily's Cake

Aunt Emily (1922-2001) was the former Emily Critch of Cavendish, NL. She married Jesse Crocker and lived the rest of her life in Heart's Delight. This dark fruitcake was a favourite of hers. She had made it many times and knew the ingredients off by heart. One day, I asked her to recite it for me. She did so willingly. I wrote it down and have used it many times since – with fond memories of Aunt Emily. Submitted by Ruby Legge, Green's Harbour.

3	cups	flour
1 1/2	tsp	baking powder
1	tsp	baking soda
3	Tbsp	cocoa powder
1	tsp	vanilla
1/2	tsp	cloves
1/2	tsp	allspice
1	lb	dates, chopped
1		package of raisins
1		package of red cherries
1/2	lb	mixed peel, finely chopped
1/2	cup	walnuts, ground (optional)
3		eggs
2	cups	brown sugar
1/2	lb	butter
2	cups	water

Procedure

In a pot add the brown sugar, butter, water, dates, raisins, cherries, and mixed peel. Bring to a boil and then let simmer for 15 minutes. Let cool.

Preheat your oven to 300°.

Take 1 cup of flour and combine with baking soda, baking powder, cocoa, and spices. Add to the cooled fruit mixture. Add the eggs and whisk into the batter, then add the nuts. Gradually add the remaining 2 cups of flour.

Bake in a greased pan at 300° for 30 minutes, and then at 275° for 1 1/2 to 2 hours or until done.

Dark and delicious! Great for Christmas, birthdays, or weddings.

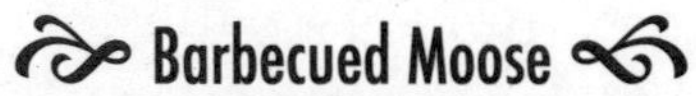

Barbecued Moose

Did you know? Newfoundland's provincial bird is the Atlantic puffin.

1/2 cup ketchup
1/2 cup vinegar
1/2 cup water
1 tsp mustard
2 tsp sugar
2 tsp Worcestershire sauce
salt and pepper to taste

Procedure

Boil the ingredients together in a pot and then add to a partially broiled moose roast or moose steaks.

Doris Garland's Fish Batter Recipe

Doris made us a meal of fish and chips and this was a real star. The batter is light and moist and is not too heavy for cod or haddock fillets. We had to have this recipe for the cookbook and share it with others. Thanks Doris!

1 cup water
1/4 cup milk
1 cup flour
1 tsp baking powder
3 Tbsp sugar

Procedure

Mix water, milk and sugar in a bowl. Add a little flour to the baking powder in another bowl. Add the dry ingredients the wet ingredients and then add the remaining flour.

Dredge your fish fillets in the batter and deep fry until golden brown.

Fried Cod Tongues

Cod tongues are the best made during the food fishery in the summer months when you can get them fresh. However, you can make this recipe with frozen cod tongues. A Newfoundland delicacy.

2	lbs	cod tongues
1 1/2	tsp	salt
1/2	cup	flour
1/4	lb	salt pork

Procedure

Put flour, salt and pepper in a plastic bag, add the cod tongues and shake. Cut up salt pork and fry until fat is rendered out, and pork strips are crisp and brown.

Remove pork strips from pan and fry tongues over medium heat until brown on both sides.

George Family Jiggs' Dinner

Todd recalls, "This is a stand-alone dinner in itself or it can be combined with what we call Sunday Dinner." This recipe was given to us by Marina (George) Warren.

3	lbs	salt beef
1/4	lb	salt pork
1/2	lb	carrots, peeled and sliced lengthwise
1		turnip, peeled and cut into large chunks (half-moon shape)
1		cabbage, cut into 1/4 sections
1		package of split yellow peas
		potatoes, enough for the family
		pease pudding bag

Procedure

Cover salt beef in a pot with cold water and soak overnight.

Drain the pot and add fresh cold water, add salt pork. Wash the peas and place in a pease pudding bag. Add to the pot.

Bring the pot to a boil. Reduce heat to medium-low for 2 hours.

Add potatoes, carrots, turnip, and cabbage wedges. Cook for 30 minutes and then serve when vegetables are cooked through.

Figgy Duff

3	cups	bread crumbs
1	cup	raisins
1/2	cup	brown sugar
1/4	tsp	salt
1/4	cup	butter, melted
1	tsp	ginger
1	tsp	allspice
1	tsp	cinnamon
3	Tbsp	molasses
1	tsp	baking soda
1	Tbsp	water, hot
1/3	cup	white flour

Procedure

In a bowl soak the bread crumbs in the hot water. Squeeze out any left-over water and bread crumb mixture, retaining the moist bread crumbs. You can squeeze the mixture with your hand, and rub your hands together with the mixture between your hands to ensure most of the water is removed. Ensure that you have 1 cup of bread crumbs after the water is removed.

In a bowl mix bread crumbs, raisins, sugar, salt and spices and mix. Add butter and molasses. Mix the baking soda and hot water in a measuring cup and then add to the mixture. Now add the flour and mix.

Put the mixture into a dampened pudding bag and tie it off securely. Boil for 1 1/2 hours.

Marina Warren's Moose Meat Loaf

Did you know? Newfoundland is inhabited by 120,000 moose – less, of course, the one used for this meat loaf recipe.

1	lb	moose meat, minced
2	Tbsp	onion, finely chopped
1		egg
1	Tbsp	salt
1/8	Tbsp	pepper
1	Tbsp	Worcestershire sauce
1/4	cup	ketchup
2/3	cups	bread crumbs

Procedure

Mix all together and pack in a loaf pan. Bake in a 325° oven for 1 hour and let meat loaf stand for 5 minutes before slicing.

Hearty Newfoundland Carrot Muffins

These are a favourite of Todd's dad, Max.

1/2	cup	flour
1/2	cup	natural wheat bran
1/2	cup	oat bran
1	tsp	baking powder
1/2	tsp	nutmeg
1/2	tsp	salt
1	tsp	cinnamon
1/2	cup	brown sugar (packed)
1		egg
1/2	cup	low fat milk
1/4	cup	butter or cooking oil
1 1/2	cups	carrot, finely grated
1/2	cup	raisins

Procedure

In a large bowl combine flour, wheat bran, oat bran, baking powder, cinnamon, nutmeg and salt and blend in brown sugar until no lumps remain.

Stir together egg, milk, and butter. Stir in carrots and then pour all at once over dry ingredients. Sprinkle with raisins and stir just until moistened – but not over-mixed.

Spoon into greased muffin pans or in muffin cups, bake at 375° for about 25 minutes or until lightly browned.

Recipe Tips

These muffins are an excellent source of vitamin A and good source of dietary fibre.

Hudson & Bridge's Dog Treat Recipe

We make these dog treats for Hudson and Bridges, our two wonderful miniature schnauzers. They were named Hudson after Mr. Angus Hudson, and Bridges after Mrs. Kate Bridges from the Upstairs Downstairs TV show by Masterpiece Theatre. They love these treats.

2 1/2	cups	whole wheat flour
1/2	cup	powdered milk
1	tsp	salt
1	tsp	sugar
1/4	tsp	garlic powder
1		egg, beaten
6	Tbsp	vegetable oil
2		small jars of beef or chicken baby food (pureed)
8	Tbsp	water

Procedure

Preheat your oven to 375°. In a large bowl combine all ingredients and mix well. Knead the mixture on a floured surface for about 5 minutes. Roll out to 1/2" thick.

Lightly spray a cookie sheet. Cut the dough with a doggy-shaped cookie cutter. Prick the top of each doggy treat with a fork and then put in oven for 30 minutes. Cool the cookies and then put in a sealed container and store in fridge or freezer.

Lobster Bisque

We were fortunate to have food writer Amy Rosen, from* The National Post*, visit us a few years ago. She sampled our lobster bisque and gave us a great review in* The National Post*. Here is a version of that recipe that is easy to prepare and has been a perennial guest favourite.

2	cups	lobster meat (fresh or frozen, thawed)
6	Tbsp	butter (no substitutes)
3	Tbsp	flour
3	cups	cream
2	oz	sherry
	pinch	paprika
1	tsp	sea salt
	pinch	cayenne pepper to taste

Procedure

In a pot melt the butter, add the lobster meat and cook over medium heat for 4 minutes, stirring constantly so the lobster meat doesn't burn.

Stir in the flour and add the cream and a dash of cayenne. Stir constantly until the soup is thickened and temperature becomes hot.

Add the sherry just before serving and stir. Ladle to bowls and add a dusting of paprika.

Marina's Curried Salt Cod Salad

Todd loves it when his mom, Marina, makes this special salt cod salad. A nice chilled salad with a barbecue.

1	lb	salt cod, cooked
1		red apple, unpeeled and diced
1/2	cup	onion, finely chopped
1/2	cup	mayonnaise
1	Tbsp	lemon juice
1/2	cup	raisins
1	tsp	curry powder

Procedure

Flake the salt cod in a bowl. Sprinkle lemon juice over diced apple. Combine apple, raisins, and onions and add salt cod. Mix well and add curry powder and salad dressing. Combine mixture and toss lightly and garnish with lettuce and red pimentos.

Moose Asian Style

This recipe was submitted to us by Marina Warren, Todd's mom. She can do just about anything with moose meat. Here is another great example of a tasty Newfoundland favourite.

3	lbs	moose meat
1/2	cup	brown sugar
1 1/2	tsp	chili powder
10	tsp	vinegar
2	cups	stewed tomatoes, undrained
2	tsp	soy sauce
1/2	tsp	ginger
2	cups	pineapple, crushed and undrained
1/2	tsp	dry mustard
2		onions, coarsely chopped
2	cups	water
1		green pepper, chopped
2	tsp	salt
6	tsp	cornstarch

Procedure

In a large pot brown the moose meat. Add all but the last ingredient to the pot and bring to a boil. Reduce the heat to low and simmer for 2 hours.

Mix the cornstarch with a little bit of cold water in a bowl to create a thin paste. Slowly drizzle the mixture into the pot and stir well. The mixture will thicken up a little and then it is ready to serve.

Nan Warren's Raisin Tea Buns

All of Nan Warren's grandchildren loved these tea buns. She made them almost every day and they were best eaten warm or hot with butter and molasses.

2	cups	flour
1/3	cup	sugar
4	tsp	baking powder
3/4	tsp	salt
1/2	cup	butter (no substitutes)
1	cup	raisins
1		egg
3/4	cups	milk

Procedure

Combine flour, sugar, baking powder and salt in a bowl. Cut in butter until crumbly. Add egg and raisins and stir. Make a well in the centre of the mixture and add the milk and mix well with a wooden spoon. Roll out the dough on a lightly floured surface. Cut out and place biscuits on an non-greased cookie sheet. Bake in a 325° oven for 20 minutes.

Newfoundland Bologna Casserole

It has been quite some time since we've feasted on this dish.

1	cup	elbow macaroni, cooked and drained
1		onion, chopped
1		green pepper, chopped
1	cup	mushrooms, sliced
1	Tbsp	butter (no substitutes)
1	lb	bologna, cubed
1	can	cream of mushroom soup (condensed)
1/2	cup	cheddar cheese, shredded (old-aged preferred)

Procedure

Preheat oven to 400°. In a large frying pan sauté the onion, green pepper, and mushrooms in butter until tender.

Transfer cooked vegetables to an ovenproof dish, add macaroni, bologna, cheese, and cream of mushroom soup. Stir well.

Cover and bake for 30 minutes and serve hot!

Salt Pork Buns

Marina Warren, Todd's mom, submitted this recipe. They are a favourite of Todd's dad, Max Warren, and no cookbook produced in Newfoundland would be complete without this recipe. They are best served with soup, such as moose soup or stew, warm with butter on them.

1	cup	salt pork, finely chopped
4	cups	flour
8	tsp	baking powder
1/2	cup	margarine
1/2	cup	molasses
1 1/2	cups	water

Procedure

Fry out the salt pork. Sift the dry ingredients into a bowl. Cut in margarine, add scrunchions (fried salt pork) and mix with a fork until the pork is well scattered.Combine molasses and water, and this to the flour mixture and stir lightly. Roll out onto a floured surface to 1/2" thickness. Cut into desired shapes, place on floured baking sheet.

Bake at 400° for 15 minutes.

Saturday's Cabin Moose Soup

Marina, Todd's mom, makes this soup just about every Saturday in the fall and winter when she is home or at the cabin. You know when she has a pot of this on the stove as you can smell the goodness when you drive in her driveway.

2 1/2	lbs	moose meat, cut into 1″ cubes
1		large onion, chopped
1		turnip, peeled and cut into 1/2″ cubes
1/2	cup	rice, not instant rice
2		potatoes, peeled and cut into 1/2″ cubes
12	cups	water
3		carrot, diced
2		parsnips, peeled and diced
1/2	tsp	salt

Procedure

In a large pot add the water and moose meat with the onion and boil for 1 hour. Add all the vegetables and simmer for 30 minutes. Add the rice and continue to cook for another 20 minutes. Now it's ready to serve.

George HOUSE

HERITAGE BED & BREAKFAST

DESSERTS & SWEET NIBBLES

Applesauce Cake

Dale remembers his mom making this cake and she always used her own homemade applesauce that she would make in the fall and freeze – it always had a real cinnamon flavour.

1/2	cup	shortening
2	cups	sugar
1/2	cup	water
2		eggs, lightly beaten
1 1/2	cups	applesauce
2	cups	flour
1 1/2	tsp	baking powder
1 1/2	tsp	baking soda
1	tsp	salt
3/4	tsp	cinnamon
1/2	tsp	cloves
1/2	tsp	allspice
1	cup	raisins
1/2	cup	nuts, chopped

Procedure

Preheat your oven to 350°. In a bowl cream together your shortening and sugar. Add water, eggs, and applesauce and cream the mixture. In a separate bowl combine the flour, baking powder, baking soda, salt, cinnamon, cloves, and allspice.

Add the dry mixture into the wet mixture and then stir in the raisins and nuts. Pour the batter into a 9" square span and bake for 35-40 minutes.

Recipe Tips

Sift a little flour or cornstarch on cake layers before icing, and icing will not run off the cake.

Baked Lemon Pudding Cake

The rooms were fabulous, very clean and beautifully decorated. The view was great and breakfast was excellent. – Guest

3		eggs
1/4	cup	butter, melted
1	cup	sugar
1/3	cup	flour
1/3	cup	lemon juice
		zest of 1 medium lemon, grated
1	cup	milk, warmed
		raspberries (optional)
		whipped cream (optional)
		mint leaves (optional)

Procedure

Preheat your oven to 350°. Separate eggs by putting the egg whites in a small bowl and the egg yolks in a large bowl. Beat the egg yolks with the melted butter and 1/2 cup of the sugar. Now add the flour and lemon juice to the large bowl a little bit at a time until it is all incorporated. Mix in the grated lemon zest.

In the bowl with the egg whites beat the whites until foamy. Now add 1/2 cup of sugar and beat until glossy and stiff peaks form. Add warm milk to the egg yolk mixture and then fold egg whites into the egg yolk mixture.

Spray or lightly butter or grease a 2- or 3-quart round, ovenproof bowl or casserole dish. Pour the batter into the bowl. Set the bowl into a pan of hot water and bake for 45 minutes or until the top is slightly browned. Spoon into individual serving dishes and garnish with raspberries.

Optional: Top with whipped cream and a fresh mint leaf.

Boiled Raisin Cake

Todd remembers his mom making these cakes and giving them as gifts to relatives during the holidays. However, this cake is great year-round and a crowd pleaser.

1 1/2	cups	raisins
3	cups	cold water
2	cups	sugar
6	Tbsp	cocoa powder
1	cup	butter (no substitutes)
1	tsp	cinnamon
1	tsp	cloves, ground
1	tsp	baking soda
1/2	cup	cold water
4	cups	flour
1	tsp	salt
1	tsp	baking powder

Procedure

Preheat your oven to 300°. In a large pot add raisins, cold water, sugar, cocoa powder, butter, cinnamon and cloves and bring to a boil for 20 minutes. Let mixture cool. In a bowl mix together baking soda and 1/2 cup cold water and add to the cooled mixture.

Add the flour, salt and baking powder to the bowl and ensure everything is incorporated well by stirring by hand.

Pour into a sprayed cake pan and bake in a 300° oven for 1 1/2 hours or until cooked using the toothpick test.

Recipe Tips

This cake can be served as is or it can be iced.

Brigus Blueberry Coffee Cake

The hosts were warm and gracious, took great pride in their B&B, were attentive to their guests and ran a first-class establishment. – Guest

1		package blueberry muffin mix
1/3	cup	sour cream
1		egg
2/3	cup	powdered sugar
1/2	cup	water
1	Tbsp	water

Procedure

In a bowl sift the muffin mix from the blueberries in the package mix. Keep separate. In a bowl stir the muffin mix with the sour cream, egg, and the 1/2 cup of water.

Rinse the blueberries that were taken from the muffin mix, drain them and gently fold them into the batter.

Spray an 11"x7" baking dish with vegetable spray and pour batter mix into the dish. Bake in a 400° oven for about 25 minutes and remove and let cool.

In a bowl mix the powdered sugar with 1 tablespoon of water and drizzle over the warm coffee cake.

Cupids Celebration Cake

The immaculate condition of the house, the splendid decor, the updated washroom, the food preparation and presentation; and the exceptional hospitality overall made our stay. – Guest

2	cups	flour
2	cups	sugar
1	tsp	baking powder
1	tsp	baking soda
1 1/2	tsp	apple pie spice
1/4	tsp	salt
2	cups	carrot, coarsely shredded
1	cup	apple, peeled and finely shredded
3/4	cup	cooking oil
4		eggs
1/2	cup	mixed nuts, chopped
1	cup	whipping cream
1	cup	sour cream
2	Tbsp	brown sugar
1	tsp	vanilla

Procedure

CAKE

Preheat oven to 350°. Spray two 9"x1 1/2" round baking pans.

In a large mixing bowl combine flour, sugar, baking powder, baking soda, apple pie spice, and salt. Add carrot, shredded apple, nuts, cooking oil, and eggs. Beat with an electric mixer at low speed until combined. Beat 1 minute at medium speed. Pour batter into prepared pans, spreading evenly.

Bake cake layers in oven for 30 minutes or until a toothpick inserted near the centre comes out clean. Let cool in pans on a wire rack for 10 minutes. Remove from pans and cool completely.

FROSTING

In a food processor place the whipping cream, sour cream, brown sugar, and vanilla and process for 2 1/2 minutes or until stiff peaks form, stopping to scrape down sides every 30 seconds.

Recipe Tips

A teaspoon of vinegar in your frosting will keep it from breaking when the frosted cake is sliced.

Coconut Carrot Cake

These cakes are wonderful as they are easy to make, are not too sweet, and they store well and keep for a few days, so they are great to have when company is around.

1	cup	vegetable oil
2	cups	sugar
3		eggs
2	cups	flour
2 1/2	tsp	baking soda
2	tsp	cinnamon
1	tsp	salt
1 1/3	cups	coconut, flaked
2	cups	carrot, shredded
1	cup	pineapple, crushed and undrained
1/2	cup	nuts, chopped

Procedure

Preheat your oven to 350°. In a bowl beat your oil, sugar, and eggs. Add your flour, baking soda, cinnamon, and salt and beat until smooth. Add coconut, carrots, pineapple and nuts.

Pour mixture into sprayed 9"x13" pan and bake for 50-60 minutes. Frost when cool.

Recipe Tips

Many of our guests have allergies to nuts, so we've often made this and substituted the chopped nuts with raisins or Craisins.

Day's End Coffee Cake

This taste-tempter will win rave reviews at a holiday brunch.

CAKE

1 1/4	cups	maraschino cherries
1	cup	cream cheese, softened
1/2	cup	slivered almonds
1/2	cup	sugar
1/2	tsp	almond extract
2		packages of crescent rolls from the dairy section of the grocery store

FROSTING

1/2	cup	icing sugar
1 1/2	tsp	milk
1/4	tsp	almond extract

Procedure

Drain the maraschino cherries and discard the juice. Keep 8-10 maraschino cherries for a garnish and chop the remaining cherries. Combine chopped cherries, cream cheese, almonds, sugar, and almond extract in a bowl and mix well.

Separate each can of crescent roll dough into 2 rectangles; press firmly at edges and perforations to make one large rectangle. Roll or pat into a rectangle about 13"x15".

Spread cream cheese mixture over dough. Roll up dough starting at long side of rectangle. Place seam-side down on a sprayed baking sheet. Form into a ring, firmly pressing ends together. With a sharp knife cut almost through ring at 1" intervals. Turn each section slightly on its side.

Bake in a preheated 350° oven 20-25 minutes or until golden brown. If necessary, cover with foil during last 5 minutes to prevent over browning. Carefully remove from pan to wire rack.

Combine icing sugar, milk and almond extract to make a glaze. Drizzle over coffee cake. Garnish with reserved whole cherries.

Florence's Rhubarb Cake

Every year we are pleased to get rhubarb from Florence George of South Dildo. Her rhubarb is some of the best in the area and we use it in many recipes. This is a favourite one of ours – we've named the recipe Florence's Rhubarb Cake in her honour.

Topping

1/2	cup	sugar
1	tsp	cinnamon
1	Tbsp	butter
1/2	cup	mixed nuts, chopped

Batter

1/2	cup	butter, softened
1 1/2	cups	brown sugar
1		egg
1	cup	sour cream
1	tsp	baking soda
2	cups	flour
1/2	tsp	salt
2	cups	fresh rhubarb, cut into 1/2 cubes
1	tsp	vanilla

Procedure

Preheat your oven to 350° and spray a 9"x13" glass baking dish.

In a bowl mix all the ingredients for the topping and set aside for the last step of the recipe.

In a large bowl cream together the butter and brown sugar. Add the egg and mix well.

In a separate bowl combine the sour cream and baking soda. Sift 1/2 the flour and 1/2 the salt into the egg and butter mixture, sift the other 1/2 of the flour and 1/2 of the salt into the sour cream mixture.

Mix the two bowls into one and add the rhubarb and vanilla and mix well. Spoon the batter into the baking dish and sprinkle the topping over the batter.

Bake the cake for 35-40 minutes and then cool on a wire rack.

Lois's Dark Fruitcake

Every year Dale lived in Nova Scotia he would receive a wonderful gift of a homemade fruitcake from Lois Eddy. While we have tried to replicate it without her recipe – this comes very close and is a wonderful cake to have with a hot cup of tea.

1	cup	raisins
1	cup	fruit peel
1	cup	mixed dried fruit, chopped
1/2	cup	dates, chopped
2	cups	sugar
1	tsp	vanilla
1/4	tsp	salt
1	cup	butter, softened
1	tsp	cinnamon
1	tsp	allspice
1/2	tsp	cloves, ground
2 1/4	cups	water
3	Tbsp	cocoa powder
1/4	cup	Screech (or black rum)
3 1/2	cups	flour
2	tsp	baking soda

Procedure

Boil all the ingredients, EXCEPT for the flour and baking soda, for 10 minutes. Cool this mixture overnight.

In the morning preheat the oven to 300°. Add the flour and baking soda to the batter and mix well. Pour into sprayed fruitcake pan and bake for 2 1/2-3 hours.

Recipe Tips

Use cocoa rather than flour to dust pans for chocolate cakes.

Once Upon A Time Molasses Cake

The service was exceptional and beyond the normal.
The decor was wonderful. – Guest

1	cup	sugar
1	cup	molasses
1	cup	vegetable oil
1	cup	boiling water
2 1/2	cups	flour
2		eggs
2	tsp	baking soda
1	tsp	cinnamon
1	tsp	ginger
1/4	cup	raisins
1/4	cup	dates, chopped

Procedure

Preheat your oven to 350°. In a glass bowl beat your eggs until foamy and add the sugar and beat well. Add the vegetable oil and beat well. Add the molasses and beat well. Now add baking soda and spice and mix well. Add flour, raisins and dates and mix well.

Pour batter into sprayed cake pan and bake in a 350° oven for 1 1/2 hours.

Recipe Tips

As the recipe says, use a really clean glass bowl so the eggs will beat foamy. Plastic bowls will not work for this recipe.

Indispensable Vanilla Cheesecake Base

Todd often serves this with bakeapple jam, partridgeberry jam or strawberry rhubarb jam.

Cheesecake Crust

1	cup	flour
$1/2$	cup	sugar
1	tsp	lemon peel, grated
$1/2$	cup	butter (no substitutes)
1		egg yolk, lightly beaten
$1/2$	tsp	vanilla

Cheesecake Filling

5	cups	cream cheese, softened
$1/2$	tsp	vanilla
$3/4$	tsp	lemon peel
$1\,3/4$	cups	sugar
3	Tbsp	flour
$1/2$	tsp	salt
5		eggs, equal to 1 cup of egg
2		egg yolks
$1/2$	cup	whipping cream

Procedure

To make the crust combine flour, sugar and lemon peel. Cut in butter until the mixture is crumbly. Add beaten egg yolk and vanilla and incorporate fully. Press $1/3$ of the mixture on the bottom of a 9" springform pan. Bake in 400° oven for 8 minutes and the base should be golden when removed from the oven. Cool the base. When cool butter the sides of the springform pan. Press remaining $2/3$ of the mixture to the sides of springform pan up $1\,1/2$" from the bottom of the pan.

Take the room temperature cream cheese and beat with a hand mixer until really creamy. Add vanilla and lemon peel and beat. Mix in sugar, flour, and salt. One at a time add the eggs and egg yolks, ensuring to thoroughly beat them into the mixture. Hand stir in the whipping cream.

Pour the mixture into the springform pan and bake at 450° for 10-12 minutes. Reduce heat to 300° and bake for an additional 55 minutes. Remove from oven and place springform pan on a cooling rack. Loosen sides of cake to pan with a spatula after having been cooled for 1/2 hour. After 1 hour remove springform sides and allow an additional hour to cool.

This cheesecake base is ideal and can be served topped with canned pie filling, fresh berries and whipped cream or a wonderful fresh fruit coulis.

Recipe Tips

If you are going through the effort to make this wonderful cheesecake base then don't use canned whipping cream – buy real whipping cream and add a touch of Frangelico or Bailey's to it and you'll love it.

Lucy's Boiled Gumdrop Cake

Dale remembers his mom making all kinds of fruitcakes and this one was very popular. She was such a baker that she would often store excess cakes, cookies, and other delights in their travel trailer in the winter once the deep freeze was full. It was a chore for one of us kids to have to go outside to the travel trailer on the cold winter days and get some sweets to put on a plate so they could thaw, and we'd enjoy them after dinner. The unheated travel trailer was like a bakeshop on wheels!

2	cups	sugar
1	cup	butter (no substitutes)
1 1/2	cups	raisins
2	cups	boiling water
1/8	tsp	salt
2	tsp	cinnamon
1	tsp	nutmeg
1	tsp	clove
2	tsp	baking soda
1	cup	gumdrops, chopped
3 1/2	cups	flour

Procedure

Preheat your oven to 350°. In a large pot mix sugar, butter, raisins, boiling hot water, salt, cinnamon, nutmeg and cloves and bring to a boil for 5 minutes.

Add 2 tsp of baking soda while the mixture is still hot. Let mixture cool completely.

Add gumdrops and flour and mix well. Pour into a sprayed cake pan and bake in a 350° oven for 2 1/2-3 hours or when cooked to a toothpick test.

Lucy's Dark Fruitcake

This recipe was a favourite to make in the fall by Dale's mom. People often joke that they "re-gift" fruitcakes, but this is one that you'll make and not want to give away.

2	cups	raisins
1	cup	butter (no substitutes)
2	cups	currants
1	cup	cherries, pitted, drained and coarsely chopped
1	cup	mixed nuts, chopped
1/2	cup	mixed dried fruit, chopped
1	cup	dates, chopped
2	cups	water
1	tsp	vanilla
1	tsp	cinnamon
1	tsp	allspice
1	tsp	cloves
2	cups	brown sugar
3	cups	flour
2	tsp	baking soda

Procedure

In a large pot add all ingredients except for the flour and baking soda and bring to a simmer and then continue to simmer for an additional 20 minutes. Allow mixture to cool completely.

Add the flour and baking soda and mix well. Pour into a sprayed cake pan and bake in a 325° oven for 2 1/2 hours or until done using toothpick test.

Maude's Berry Butter Cake

This is a true favourite of all guests that stay at the B&B and we make a fresh berry butter cake each and every day all summer using fresh or frozen local partridgeberries or blueberries. This recipe was given to Todd by Maude Williams of Dildo.

1	cup	sugar
1	cup	flour
3/4	cup	butter, melted
2		eggs
1	tsp	vanilla
1	cup	blueberries or partidgeberries

Procedure

Mix flour and sugar together in a bowl.

Add 2 eggs, vanilla, and melted butter and stir well.

Put your fresh or frozen berries in a 9"x12" glass baking dish – enough to cover the bottom of the dish

Pour batter over the berries without mixing the berries into the batter.

Put in a preheated oven at 350° for 50 minutes for frozen berries and 40 minutes for fresh berries.

Cake will be lightly golden brown when fully baked.

Cut cake into squares and serve warm or cold. Ideal with whipped cream or Todd's Brown Sugar Rum Sauce (see recipe page 253).

Recipe Tips

Keep the berry butter cake in the dish until you are ready to serve it. This can be warmed in microwave if you wish to serve it hot.

Pineapple Carrot Cake

Todd notes that this recipe was made many times for parties at the B&B and it is so yummy served with cream cheese icing. This recipe came from Nina Snow and was passed from her to her son and then onto us.

1 1/2	cups	flour
1	cup	sugar
1	tsp	baking powder
1	tsp	baking soda
1	tsp	cinnamon
1/2	tsp	salt
2/3	cup	vegetable oil
2		eggs
1	cup	carrot, finely grated
1/2	cup	pineapple, crushed and undrained
1	tsp	vanilla
1/2	cup	walnuts, chopped

Procedure

Preheat your oven to 350°. In a large bowl mix together flour, sugar, baking powder, baking soda, cinnamon and salt. Add the vegetable oil, eggs, carrot, crushed pineapple, vanilla, and walnuts.

Mix until blended and then beat it with a hand mixer or stand mixer at medium for 2 minutes.

Pour mixture into a sprayed tube pan and bake for 40 minutes or until cake springs back to the touch. Let cool for 5 minutes before removing from tube pan.

Recipe Tips

While this cake calls for a tube pan it can be baked in a 9" square pan or layer pans to make a double layer cake.

Pineapple Upside-Down Cake

This has been a sought-after favourite by the guests at the B&B and is a timeless classic

Topping

2	Tbsp	butter, melted
1/2	cup	brown sugar
1	can	pineapple slices canned in own juice
8		maraschino cherries

Cake

1/3	cup	shortening
1 1/4	cups	flour
1/2	cup	sugar
2	tsp	baking powder
1/2	tsp	salt
1/2	cup	pineapple juice from the can
1/2	tsp	lemon peel, grated
1		egg
		whipped cream (optional)

Procedure

In a 8"x8" baking dish add melted butter. Add brown sugar and stir. spread evenly over bottom of the dish. Add as many pineapple rings that will layout evenly across the bottom of the baking dish. Place a cherry in the middle of each pineapple ring.

To make the cake stir softened shortening and sift in the flour, sugar, baking powder and salt. Add pineapple syrup, lemon peel and egg. Mix until all is incorporated and then beat for 2 minutes. Pour cake batter evenly over pineapple slices.

Bake at 350° for 30-35 minutes until done. Let stand 10 minutes and then invert on a cookie sheet. Each pineapple ring makes 1 serving and is best served warm with a large dollop of whipping cream.

Screech & Rum Cake

Warmth of welcome from Dale and Todd. – Guest

1	cup	butter (no substitutes)
1/2	cup	brown sugar
3		eggs
1	cup	molasses
3 1/2	cups	flour
1	cup	milk
1/4	cup	Screech (or any style good rum)
1	cup	cherries, pitted, drained and coarsely chopped
2	tsp	baking powder
1	tsp	baking soda
1	tsp	cinnamon
1/2	tsp	clove
1	tsp	allspice
1/4	cup	steeped tea
1	cup	raisins
1	cup	currants

Procedure

Preheat your oven to 325°. In a large bowl cream the butter and sugar together. Add the eggs, molasses and spices and mix well. Add the milk, tea and rum and mix well. Add all the remaining ingredients and mix well.

Pour batter into a sprayed cake pan and bake at 325° for 2 hours.

Simple Simon's Cheesecake

The very high quality of the rooms and the whole inn; the warm, friendly welcome; the fabulous food and the atmosphere of ease, comfort and pride that the owners take in their INN. Wonderful. The best we experienced in NL and that's saying a lot. – Guest

2	cups	cream cheese, softened
1/2	cup	sugar
1/2	tsp	vanilla
2		eggs
1		9″ graham cracker pie shell, unbaked

Procedure

Preheat your oven to 350°. In a bowl beat the cream cheese, sugar, vanilla, and eggs. Pour the mixture into the pie shell. Bake for 40 minutes and then let cool. Once cool, place in the fridge to chill.

Add any favourite canned fruit pie filling as a topping and enjoy.

Standard Pound Cake

Beautiful surroundings; very helpful and friendly staff. – Guest

1	cup	butter, softened
2	cups	sugar
5		eggs
2	cups	flour
1	Tbsp	almond extract

Procedure

Preheat your oven to 325°. In a bowl combine all the ingredients and beat for 10 minutes with a hand mixer.

Pour into a greased and floured tube pan. Bake for 1 hour and use the toothpick test to check to see if it is fully baked as the pound cake is a very thick batter.

Recipe Tips

We use this pound cake for tea service or you can drizzle it with lemon drizzle and add a scoop of vanilla ice cream to make a great dessert.

To make lemon drizzle put juice of 1 1/2 lemons and 1/4 cup of icing sugar and stir well. Pierce the top of the pound cake with a fork and then using a spoon drizzle the lemon drizzle over the cake – some of the icing will seep into the holes make by the fork and the remainder will drizzle down the sides of the cake.

Tammy Boyer's Hopeall Coffee Cake

This recipe was given to us by staff member Tammy Boyer. This is more of a blueberry cake than a coffee cake according to Tammy but we love it and had to name it after her.

3/4	cup	sugar
1/4	cup	butter (no substitutes)
1		egg
1	tsp	vanilla
1/2	cup	milk
1/4	cup	water
1 3/4	cups	flour
1/2	tsp	salt
3	tsp	baking powder
1 1/2	cups	blueberries
1 1/2	tsp	sugar

Topping

2	Tbsp	brown sugar
1/2	tsp	cinnamon

Procedure

In a bowl cream the 3/4 cup of sugar, 1/4 cup of butter and 1 egg and 1 teaspoon of vanilla.

Add the milk, water, flour, salt and baking powder and mix well.

Spread 1/2 of the mixture in a ovenproof baking dish and then sprinkle the blueberries over the batter. Now sprinkle the 1 1/2 tsp of sugar over the berries.

Gently spread the rest of the batter over the blueberries.

In a separate bowl mix the 2 tablespoons of brown sugar and cinnamon and then sprinkle over the top of the batter.

Bake in a 350° oven for 30 minutes. Serve warm or let cool. This is ideal with some fresh whipped cream and a good cup of coffee.

Todd's Version Of Red Velvet Cake

Todd saw this cake recipe on TV one day and had to make it. He made it for a family Christmas dinner in Halifax and was very proud to present it to everyone. Not to be outdone, Todd altered the recipe and turned it into a 7-layer red velvet cake. It was the highlight of the dinner.

1/2	cup	shortening
1	cup	sugar
5		eggs or equal to 1 cup of egg
2	Tbsp	cocoa powder
1 1/2	Tbsp	red food coloring
1	tsp	vanilla
2 1/2	cups	flour
1/2	tsp	salt
1	tsp	baking soda
1	cup	buttermilk
1	Tbsp	vinegar
1	cup	whipped topping

Procedure

Heat the oven to 350°. Cream the shortening, sugar, and egg substitute together. In a small bowl, make a thick paste of the cocoa and food colouring and add it to the cream mixture. Stir in the vanilla.

Sift together the flour, salt, and baking soda. Alternately add portions of the flour mixture and the buttermilk to the creamed mixture, stirring well.

Mix in the vinegar and pour the batter into a 9"x9" or oblong pan. Bake for 30 minutes. Allow to cool. Cut into 10 squares and top each square with whipped topping.

Recipe Tips

You can make a couple of batches of this batter, pour them into round cake pans and then use a cream cheese icing to make a spectacular layer cake dessert. Garnish the perimeter of the cake with toasted sliced almonds. (Don't forget to take a photo of this cake before everyone devours it.)

Bumpy Road Cookies

Each morning for the past few years we've surprised guests by giving them a bag of freshly made cookies to take on their travels as they check out of the B&B. We make several different kinds of cookies so the guests never know what they will get in the bag. We call this recipe "Bumpy Road Cookies" in case they are travelling to the far reaches of the province.

1	cup	flour
1/2	tsp	baking soda
1/4	tsp	baking powder
1/8	tsp	salt
1/2	cup	butter, room temperature, diced
1/2	cup	sugar
1/2	cup	yellow sugar
1/2	tsp	vanilla
1	cup	rolled oats
1	cup	chocolate chips

Procedure

Preheat your oven to 350°. Spray two cookie sheets.

In a large bowl sift the flour, baking soda, baking powder and salt. In a separate bowl add butter and sugar and mix with a hand mixer. Add the egg and vanilla and beat until well incorporated.

Now add the flour mixture to the butter mixture and beat on low with electric mixer until everything is incorporated. With a wooden spoon stir in the rolled oats and chocolate chips. The dough will become crumbly.

Drop the cookie mixture by the teaspoon or very small ice cream scoop onto the sprayed cookie sheet and bake for 15 minutes.

Remove cookies from the cookie sheet and place on cookie cooling rack.

Cameron Heraldry Shortbread

The Cameron surname is thought to be derived from the Gaelic "cam-shron," meaning "crooked or hook nose," although Dale doesn't have one!

1/2	cup	butter, unsalted and softened
1/3	cup	sugar
1 1/4	cups	flour
		powdered sugar

Procedure

Preheat your oven to 325°. In a bowl cream together butter and sugar until light and fluffy. Add the flour and a dash of salt and mix well. Spread the dough into an 8" square pan and bake for 20 minutes or until lightly golden brown. Remove from oven and let shortbread cool, dust with some powdered sugar and then cut into squares.

Chocolate Nutty Kisses

Accommodations outstanding and food exceptional. – Guest

2		egg whites, room temperature
2/3	cup	sugar
1	tsp	vanilla
1 1/4	cups	walnuts, chopped
3/4	cup	chocolate chips
	pinch	salt

Procedure

Preheat the oven to 375°. In a glass bowl beat the egg whites until very stiff and then blend in the sugar, vanilla and a pinch of salt. Gently add the chopped walnuts and chocolate chips.

Cover a cookie sheet pan with aluminum foil with the shiny side up and drop the dough onto the foil by teaspoonfuls. A very small ice cream scoop is ideal for this.

Put the cookies in the oven, turn the oven off and leave the cookies in the oven overnight. Do not open the oven door. Remove the following morning and if the cookies are still a bit tacky leave them on the counter for a few hours to air-dry.

Chocolate Drop Chip

The hospitality of the owners and staff and the exceptional accommodations and food made our trip. – Guest

1/2	cup	shortening
1/2	cup	sugar
1/4	cup	brown sugar
1		egg
1	tsp	vanilla
1	cup	flour
3/4	tsp	salt
1/2	tsp	baking soda
1	cup	semisweet chocolate chips
1/2	cup	peanuts, unsalted and chopped

Procedure

In a bowl cream the shortening, white and brown sugar, egg, and vanilla until thoroughly mixed. Sift together the flour, salt and baking soda.

Stir dry mixture into wet mixture and incorporate well. Add chocolate and peanuts. Drop from a teaspoon on a sprayed or greased cookie sheet.

Bake at 375° for 10-12 minutes. Remove from oven and immediately remove cookies from cookie sheet and put on a cooling rack.

Recipe Tips

You can use this drop cookie recipe as a base and substitute raisins for nuts, or use cashews or walnuts, or at Christmas you can use lightly crushed candy canes.

Coconut Macaroons

The bedrooms were extremely lovely . . . the service was great, the food was delicious and everyone was friendly. – Guest

2		egg whites, slightly beaten
1/2	tsp	vanilla
2/3	cup	sugar
1 1/3	cups	coconut, flaked or shredded
		dash of salt

Procedure

Beat the egg whites with vanilla and a dash of salt until soft peaks form. Slowly add the sugar and beat until stiff peaks form.

Fold in the coconut and then drop by teaspoon onto greased or sprayed cookie sheet and bake at 325° for 20 minutes.

Recipe Tips

When making this recipe be sure to use fresh coconut. By using older coconut in bag that you find in the back of your cupboard or pantry, the cookies will not turn out well.

Crunchy Peanut Butter Cookies

Absolute attention to detail – the toiletries, robes, fresh cookies, beautiful breakfast presentation. – Guest

1/2	cup	butter, softened
1/4	cup	brown sugar (firmly packed)
1		egg
1	tsp	vanilla
1	cup	crunchy peanut butter
1	cup	flour
1/2	tsp	baking soda
1/8	tsp	salt

Procedure

In a large bowl add butter and sugar and then use a hand mixer to cream the ingredients together. In a separate bowl mix the egg and vanilla well and then gradually drizzle it into the butter and sugar mixture and use hand mixer to incorporate.

Stir in the peanut butter and mix thoroughly. Sift in the flour, baking soda and salt and stir into the mixture to form a soft dough. Refrigerate the dough for 30 minutes until firm.

Preheat the oven to 350° and spray two cookie sheets.

Use a spoon or very small ice cream scoop and spoon out the dough and roll into small balls. Place the balls on the cookie sheets and then use the tines of a fork to press flat.

Bake the cookies for about 12 minutes or until lightly brown. Remove from the cookie sheet and then put on a cookie cooling rack.

Easter Bunny Cookies

Happy Birthday Easter Bunny!

1/2	cup	butter, room temperature, diced
1/2	cup	sugar
1		egg, separated
1 3/4	cups	flour
1/2	tsp	apple pie spice
1/2	tsp	cinnamon
1/4	cup	currants
1	Tbsp	mixed peel, finely chopped
2	Tbsp	milk

Procedure

Preheat the oven to 400° and spray two cookie sheets.

In a bowl beat together the butter and sugar until light and fluffy and then mix in the egg yolk. In another bowl add the flour, apple pie spice and cinnamon and sift. Now take the sifted flour mixture and sift it for the second time over the butter and egg mixture. Using a wooden spoon incorporate the flour mixture into the butter mixture and then add the currants and fruit and milk to create a soft dough.

On a floured surface turn out the dough and knead until smooth then roll out the dough using a rolling pin until very thin, about 1/4" thick. Using a round cookie cutter cut out cookies and transfer them to the cookie sheets and bake for 10 minutes.

Beat the egg white in a clean bowl and then remove cookies at the 10 minute mark. Brush the egg whites over the cookies and sprinkle with a little sugar and then return to the oven for an additional 10 minutes. Remove from the cookie sheet and place on a cooling rack.

Recipe Tips

When sprinkling the sugar in Step 4 you can substitute the white sugar with those coloured sugar crystals that you find in the baking isle of your local grocery store.

Easy Chocolate Chip Cookies

The George House was lovely, the products made available in the bathroom were great. Staff were very helpful and friendly. – Guest

1/4	cup	butter
1 1/2	Tbsp	sugar
1		egg
3	Tbsp	water
1	tsp	vanilla
3/4	cup	flour
1/4	tsp	baking soda
1/4	tsp	salt
1/2	cup	semi-sweet chocolate chips

Procedure

Preheat the oven to 375°. In a medium bowl, cream the butter and sugar. Beat in the egg, water, and vanilla; mix thoroughly.

In a sifter, combine the flour, baking soda, and salt. Sift the dry ingredients into the creamed mixture and mix well. Stir in the chocolate chips.

Drop teaspoonfuls of dough onto sprayed cookie sheets and bake for 8-10 minutes. Remove the cookies from the oven and cool them on racks.

Fork In The Road Sugar Cookies

The environment was comfortably elegant. – Guest

3/4	cup	brown sugar (packed)
1	cup	butter (no substitutes), softened
1		egg yolk
2	cups	flour

Procedure

Preheat the oven to 325°. In a bowl cream the sugar and butter until it is fluffy. Mix in the egg yolk and then blend flour into the mixture. Place the mixture into the fridge for 1 hour to chill.

Remove dough from fridge and form into 1" balls, flatten them and use a fork to gently press them down and create a criss-cross pattern and place on a cookie sheet.

Bake the cookies at 325° for 10-12 minutes or until golden brown. Let cook on a cookie rack.

Gingerbread, Gingerbread!

Kids love them and so do adults – they taste good, are fun to decorate and are again a timeless classic.

1/2	cup	shortening
1/2	cup	sugar
1	tsp	baking powder
1	tsp	ginger, ground
1/2	tsp	baking soda
1/2	tsp	cinnamon, ground
1/2	tsp	cloves, ground
1/2	cup	molasses
1		egg
1	Tbsp	vinegar
2 1/2	cups	flour

Procedure

In a mixing bowl beat shortening with an electric mixer on medium to high speed 30 seconds. Add sugar, baking powder, ginger, baking soda, cinnamon, and cloves. Beat until combined, scraping bowl. Beat in the molasses, egg, and vinegar until combined. Beat in as much of the flour as you can with the mixer. Stir in remaining flour.

Divide dough in half. Cover and chill in the fridge for 3 hours or until easy to handle. Grease a cookie sheet and set aside.

On a lightly floured surface, roll half of the dough at a time to 1/8" thick. Using a 2 1/2" cookie cutter, cut into desired shapes. Place 1" apart on the prepared cookie sheet.

Bake in a 375° oven for 5-6 minutes or until edges are lightly browned. Cool on cookie sheet 1 minute. Transfer cookies to a wire rack and let cool. If desired, decorate cookies with icing and candies.

Granny Cookies

Everybody's grandmother has made these type of cookies at one time or another. This is another recipe that we were given on a scrap of paper and over the years has finally made it into this cookbook.

1 1/2	cups	shortening
1	cup	sugar
1	cup	brown sugar
2	eggs	
2	tsp	baking powder
2	tsp	baking soda
2	Tbsp	vinegar
2	tsp	vanilla
1	tsp	almond extract
4	cups	flour

Procedure

Preheat your oven to 350°. In a bowl cream the shortening and sugars. Add the eggs and beat the mixture well. In a separate bowl dissolve the baking powder and baking soda in vinegar and add to the creamed mixture along with the vanilla and almond extract. Mix the batter well. Add the flour to the batter and beat until well incorporated. Shape into balls and place on a greased cookie sheet. Press down with a fork and bake for 15-20 minutes. Caution: do not over bake these cookies.

Lemon Drops

Sometimes the easiest recipes are the best – no complicated ingredients, no fancy equipment need and not a ton of time required for you to make something special for someone special.

1/2	cup	butter (no substitutes), softened
1	cup	white sugar
2	Tbsp	lemon juice
2	cups	flour

Procedure

Preheat oven to 350°. In a bowl mix butter, sugar and lemon juice and then gently stir in the flour.

Drop by the tablespoon onto a cookie sheet pan. Bake at 350° for 14-15 minutes. Remove from cookie sheet and cool on cookie rack.

Holiday Sugar Cookies

I loved the lupins. Loved sitting in the brightly coloured Adirondack chairs, drinking wine in the sunshine and looking at the bay. – Guest

1/3	cup	butter, softened
1/3	cup	shortening
3/4	cup	sugar
1	tsp	baking powder
1/8	tsp	salt
1		egg
1	tsp	vanilla
2	cups	flour

Procedure

In a mixing bowl beat butter and shortening with an electric mixer on medium to high speed for 30 seconds. Add sugar, baking powder, and salt. Beat until combined, scraping sides of bowl occasionally. Beat in egg and vanilla until combined. Beat in as much of the flour as you can with the mixer. Using a wooden spoon, stir in any remaining flour.

Cover and chill about 1 hour or until dough is easy to handle.

On a lightly floured surface, roll a portion of the dough at a time to 1/8" thickness. Using a 2 1/2" cookie cutter, cut dough into desired shapes. Place cutouts on an ungreased cookie sheet. Refrigerate cutouts for 15 minutes.

Bake in a 375° oven for 7-8 minutes for smaller cookies or about 10 minutes for larger cookies or until edges are firm and bottoms are very lightly browned. Cool on cookie sheet for 1 minute. Transfer cookies to a wire rack; cool.

I Love Butter Cookies

It was a beautiful place to stay. The owner paid a lot of attention to detail and the food was excellent. I would highly recommend it. – Guest

2	cups	butter (no substitutes)
3/4	cup	brown sugar (packed)
3/4	cup	sugar
4 1/2	cups	flour

Procedure

Preheat the oven to 350°. In a bowl cream together butter, white and brown sugar and then gently add the flour and mix very well. The cookie mixture is very thick in consistency.

Roll the cookie dough into small balls and place on an ungreased cookie sheet. Bake for 15 minutes or until slightly brown. Caution: do not over bake these cookies.

Recipe Tips

Cookies continue to bake on a cookie sheet after they are removed from the oven. Watch your oven and timing to ensure you don't burn your first batch of cookies.

M&M Cookies & Bars

The rooms were fabulous, very clean and beautifully decorated. The view was great and breakfast was excellent. – Guest

1/4	cup	butter
1 1/2	cups	graham cracker crumbs
1	can	sweetened condensed milk
1 1/2	cups	coconut, shredded
2	cups	M&M's plain candy

Procedure

Preheat your oven to 325°. Melt the butter in a 9"x13" glass baking dish in the oven. Remove from the oven once the butter is melted and sprinkle the graham cracker crumbs over the butter evenly.

Pour the sweetened condensed milk over the crumbs and use a rubber spatula to ensure you get all the milk out of the can.

Sprinkle the coconut and M&M candy over the top of the mixture evenly and press firmly down with your hand. Bake in a 325° oven for 25 minutes. Cool completely and then cut into squares or bars.

Night & Day Cookies

Thanks for making us welcome and sharing part of your world with us. We've taken your hospitality and memories home to Georgia with us. If you are ever in our area please let us show you some of the South. – Guest

1		egg white
1/2	cup	sugar
1/2	cup	almonds, ground
1/2	cup	chocolate chips
1/2	cup	glazed cherries, chopped
2/3	cup	sweetened coconut, shredded

Procedure

Preheat your oven to 425°. Line a cookie sheet with parchment paper.

In a large glass bowl add the egg white and whisk until stiff peaks form. Add the sugar to the whisked egg whites a little at a time. Ensure that you whisk them together well to ensure all the sugar is incorporated into the egg whites.

Now, use an electric mixer to beat the mixture to stiff peaks.

Using a wooden spoon fold in the almonds, chocolate chips, candied cherries and coconut. Drop tablespoons full of cookie mixture onto the parchment paper making 12 cookies.

Place the cookie sheet into the oven and then turn the oven off. Leave the cookies in the oven overnight or for a minimum of 8 hours. Remove cookie sheet from the oven and they are ready to eat.

Oatcakes

Our group had a terribly wonderful visit with you and your staff. The evening spent on the lawn at sunset were stunning albeit too short. Your staff were attentive to our group and we appreciated it given our special needs. – Guest

2 1/4	cups	rolled oats
2/3	cup	flour
1/4	tsp	baking soda
1	tsp	salt
2	Tbsp	shortening
2	Tbsp	butter (no substitutes)
		boiling water

Procedure

Preheat your oven to 425°. In a large bowl mix together the rolled oats, flour, baking soda and salt. Mix well.

Melt the shortening and butter together in the microwave and add the melted shortening and butter and enough boiling water to the dry ingredients to make a dough mixture.

Turn the dough out onto a floured countertop. Roll out the dough very thin and then cut into cookie rounds.

Bake for 15 minutes in a 425° oven.

Oatmeal Raisin Cookie

Our comments are few and brief. What a gem, great accommodations, excellent location, finely decorated INN, and yummy breakfast. We enjoyed our three days and the day trips around the trails. – Guest

1	cup	butter, melted
2	cups	brown sugar
2		eggs
2	tsp	vanilla
1 1/2	cups	flour
1	tsp	salt
1	tsp	baking soda
1	tsp	cinnamon
3	cups	rolled oats
1	cup	walnuts
1	cup	raisins

Procedure

Preheat your oven to 375°. In a large bowl mix together the melted butter, brown sugar, eggs and vanilla. Sift in the flour, salt, baking soda and cinnamon and mix well. Stir in the oats, nuts and raisins.

Drop the dough by the spoonfuls onto a sprayed cookie sheet and bake for about 10 minutes. Even though the cookies may look a little undercooked take them out of the oven after the 10 minutes as they will finish cooking and firm up on the cookie sheet as they cool.

Todd's Favourite Shortbread Recipe

This recipe was given to Todd when he was searching for an easy shortbread to make for guests of the B&B. Everyone loves a couple of shortbread with a hot cup of tea at any time of the day.

3 1/2	cups	flour
1	cup	icing sugar
2	cups	butter (no substitutes), unsalted and softened
2	tsp	vanilla
		pinch of salt

Procedure

Preheat your oven to 350°. In a large bowl mix all ingredients together with a wooden spoon. Drop by the teaspoon onto an ungreased cookie sheet.

Bake in a 350° oven for 15 minutes. Be careful to make sure you don't overcook these cookies as real butter tends to burn if overcooked. Remove from cookie sheet and place on a wire cooling rack. Enjoy.

Walnut Cookies

Besides being one of the best maintained properties that we've stayed at we also thought the dining room dinner was top-notch. – Guest

1/2	cup	butter at room temperature
1	cup	sugar
1	cup	flour
2	tsp	vanilla
1	cup	walnuts, finely chopped

Procedure

Preheat your oven to 300°. Spray two cookie sheets.

In a bowl using an electric mixer cream the butter and then add 1/4 cup of the sugar and continue to beat until light and fluffy. Stir in the flour, vanilla and walnuts.

Drop teaspoonful of cookie mix onto the cookie sheets. Flatten with the tines of a fork and bake for 25 minutes until golden brown.

Remove from the cookie sheet and cool on a cookie rack. Sprinkle with remaining sugar and then let cool.

Peanut Butter Cookies

Your staff care about the guests experience at your Inn and you should be commended on this. We'll spread the word to our neighbours and friends in Ontario. – Guest

1/4	cup	butter (no substitutes)
1/4	cup	creamy peanut butter
2	Tbsp	brown sugar
1		egg
1/4	cup	water
1	tsp	vanilla
1 1/2	cups	flour
1	tsp	baking soda
1/2	tsp	baking powder

Procedure

In a food processor or by hand, cream together the butter, peanut butter, and sugar. Add the egg, water, and vanilla and continue to mix until well blended.

Combine the flour, baking soda, and baking powder in a sifter; sift dry ingredients into creamed mixture and mix until completely blended. Refrigerate overnight.

Lightly spray cookie sheets. Drop teaspoonfuls onto cookie sheets and press with the tines of a fork to flatten each cookie. Bake at 375° for 12-15 minutes. Remove from oven and let cook on cookie racks.

Dutch Apple Pie

We loved our stay – thanks for all that you did to make it special. – Guest

9″ diameter pie shell, unbaked

Filling

7		tart apples, peeled, cored and thinly sliced
1	cup	sour cream
3/4	cup	sugar
1		egg, slightly beaten
1	tsp	vanilla
1/4	tsp	nutmeg
1/4	tsp	salt
1	tsp	cinnamon
3	Tbsp	flour

Topping

1/2	cup	brown sugar (firmly packed)
1/2	cup	walnuts, finely chopped
1/2	cup	flour
1	tsp	cinnamon
3	Tbsp	butter (no substitutes)

Procedure

For the filling: place the apples in a mixing bowl. In another bowl mix together sour cream, sugar, egg, vanilla, cinnamon, nutmeg, salt and flour. Pour the mixture over the apples. Toss everything lightly.

Spoon the mixture into the pie shell.

For the topping: place the brown sugar, walnuts, flour, cinnamon and butter in a food processor and process until the results are well combined and crumbly. Sprinkle the mixture evenly over the top of the apple filling. Place in the oven and bake at 425° for 20 minutes. Reduce heat to 350° and bake for 30-40 more minutes.

Banana Pie

We've visited the banana plantations in Costa Rica and really learned a lot. Bananas are good for you as they are low in saturated fats, cholesterol and sodium. They are also a good source of dietary fibre, potassium, Vitamin B6, manganese and Vitamin C. In this recipe they just taste – delicious.

1 1/2	cups	milk
1/4	cup	sugar
1/4	cup	flour
2		eggs, lightly beaten
3		large bananas, sliced 1/4 thick
		pinch salt
1	tsp	vanilla
		9″ diameter pie shell, baked

Procedure

In a bowl mix sugar, flour and salt well. Add eggs and beat well. Add the milk and stir well.

Pour mixture into a pot and cook on medium heat until mixture thickens stirring constantly. Let mixture cool. Now add banana slices and mix gently. Pour banana mixture into a baked pie shell and serve with tons of whipped cream.

Key West Key Lime Pie

During one of our winter travels we drove to Florida and had the good fortune to visit the Florida Keys. The scenery was stunning and we thoroughly loved Key West. We couldn't leave without trying real authentic key lime pie and it was delicious. We were given this easy key lime pie recipe and every time we make it we are transported back in time to Key West.

6		egg yolks
3 1/2	cups	sweetened condensed milk
1	cup	lime juice from concentrate
1		9″ graham cracker pie shell, unbaked

Procedure

Preheat the oven to 350°. In a mixing bowl beat egg yolks with condensed milk. Gently stir in lime juice. Pour the mixture into the pie crust and bake for 20 minutes.

Let the pie cool and then chill in the fridge. Serve with fresh whipped cream or whipped topping.

Blueberry Velvetine Custard Pie

My husband raved about dinner and we enjoyed the drizzly evening watching* The Shipping News *and the experience was topped with the whale sighting. – Guest

4		eggs
2/3	cup	sugar
1/2	tsp	salt
1/2	tsp	nutmeg
2 2/3	cups	milk
1	tsp	vanilla
1		9″ deep-dish pie shell, unbaked
1	cup	blueberries
2	Tbsp	orange juice
3	Tbsp	icing sugar

Procedure

Preheat your oven to 425°. In a bowl beat the eggs with a hand mixer until thoroughly beaten. Add the sugar, salt, nutmeg, milk and vanilla and stir until smooth.

Pour mixture into the pie shell and bake for 15 minutes. Then reduce oven temperature to 350° for an additional 30 minutes.

In a bowl blend the blueberries, orange juice and icing sugar. Spoon over the custard pie before serving.

Lemon Pie Filling

This pie filling can be used in a lemon meringue pie, or tarts, or is even great used in a 9″x13″ glass baking dish over graham wafer crumbs.

1/2	cup	cornstarch
1 1/4	cups	sugar
1/4	tsp	salt
2	cups	boiling water
3		egg yolks, well-beaten
1 1/2	tsp	lemon peel, grated
1/3	cup	lemon juice, freshly squeezed
2	Tbsp	butter (no substitutes)

Procedure

In a pot mix together cornstarch, sugar and salt. Gradually stir in the water and in a double boiler cook for about 15 minutes constantly stirring until filling thickens.

Add egg yolks, lemon rind and lemon juice. Cook for an additional 2 minutes constantly stirring the filling. Add the butter and let mixture cool slightly and remove from double boiler.

Pour into pastry shell or use as you wish.

Plain Pastry Recipe

We'll definitely recommend you to everyone we can. Thanks and keep in touch. – Guest

2	cups	flour
1	tsp	salt
2/3	cup	shortening
5	Tbsp	cold water (approximate)

Procedure

In a bowl sift together flour and salt and cut in the shortening with a pastry blender. To make pastry extra flaky divide shortening in 1/2 and cut in first half until the mixture resembles cornmeal and then cut in remaining 1/2 of shortening until mixture resembles small peas.

Sprinkle 1 tablespoon of water over mixture and gently toss with a fork. Repeat this last step until all is moistened.

Gather the dough with your fingers and form into a ball, roll out on a lightly floured surface into 1/8" thick.

Wake Of The Week Pie

This is an old-fashioned pie recipe. Raisin pie is sometimes called funeral pie, because it became a tradition to serve raisin pie with the meal that was served to family and friends at a wake or following a funeral. The most likely reason for this was that it could be made at any time of the year, it kept well, and could be made a day or two before the funeral.

1	cup	raisins
2	cups	water, hot
1 1/4	cups	sugar
4	Tbsp	flour
1		egg, slightly beaten
		zest and juice of 1 lemon
1/4	tsp	salt
1	Tbsp	butter
2		8″ pie shell, unbaked

Procedure

Preheat your oven to 450°. In a bowl soak the raisins in hot water for 1 hour or longer. Drain the water off the raisins. Add the remaining ingredients and mix thoroughly.

Cook the batter mixture in a double boiler until thickened. Cool the batter. Pour into a pie shell and use the second pie shell to create pastry strips over the filing to make a lattice top.

Bake the pie in the 450° oven for 10 minutes and then lower the heat to 350° for 25 minutes or until golden brown. Bake until the pastry is nicely browned.

Pumpkin Pie

Neither of us is a big fan of pumpkin pie. However, we make it for those who do love pumpkin pie and this is a great one to serve not only at Thanksgiving but all fall and winter long.

1	can	pumpkin (should be 16-oz can)
1	can	Carnation evaporated milk
2		eggs
2/3	cup	sugar
2	tsp	pumpkin pie spice
1		9″ diameter pie shell, unbaked

Procedure

In large bowl combine pumpkin, milk, eggs, sugar and pumpkin pie spice. Pour into pie shell.

Bake at 425° for 15 minutes. Reduce oven to 350°. and bake 40-50 minutes or until knife inserted in centre comes out clean.

Recipe Tips

When putting meringue on a pie be certain the meringue touches all the crust around the pie or the meringue will shrink when baked.

Apple Crisp

Our stay was the highlight of the trip and we wish you and your staff the best of business in the future. – Guest

4		large baking apples, peeled and sliced
3/4	cup	brown sugar
1/2	cup	flour
3/4	cup	oatmeal
3/4	tsp	cinnamon
3/4	tsp	nutmeg
1/3	cup	butter or margarine

Procedure

Heat the oven to 350°. Spray a baking pan and place the apples in the pan.

Mix the brown sugar, flour, oatmeal, cinnamon, and nutmeg together and place on top of the apple. Drop dots of margarine or butter over the dry mixture. Bake for 25 minutes.

Applesauce

This applesauce can be served as a dessert on its own, with a little ice cream or whipped cream, or you can serve it with your next pork chop dinner. Add a little cinnamon if you like.

1 1/2	lbs	apples, peeled, cored and diced
1 1/2	cups	water
1/3	cup	sugar

Procedure

In a pot add the apples and water and cook until tender soft, then add the sugar and continue to cook for an additional 15 minutes.

Baked Custard

"Great beds, spick 'n span clean, great food, beyond service . . . and true Newfoundland hospitality." – Guest

3	cups	milk
3		eggs
3/4	cup	sugar
1/4	tsp	salt
1	tsp	vanilla extract
		cinnamon

Procedure

Preheat the oven to 350°. In a saucepan heat the milk to scalding. In a separate bowl beat the eggs, and then add the sugar, salt and vanilla. Slowly add the scalded milk to the egg mixture. Do this slowly, otherwise you'll end up with scrambled eggs. Pour the entire mixture into a 2-quart baking dish and sprinkle with a bit of cinnamon on top. Bake in a 350° oven in a hot water bath for 45 minutes.

Blackberry & Apple Crumble

We'll recommend you to everyone and hope to return and soon. – Guest

BASE

3		Granny Smith apples, peeled and sliced
1	lb	fresh or frozen blackberries, thawed
1/2	cup	sugar
1	tsp	cinnamon

TOP

1 1/2	cups	white flour
1 1/2	cups	brown sugar
3/4	cup	rolled oats
3/4	cup	butter, melted

Procedure

Preheat the oven to 350 degrees and coat a 9"x13" glass baking dish with non-stick cooking spray. Place the apples on the bottom of the dish and then top with the blackberries. In a bowl, mix sugar and cinnamon, sprinkle this over the blackberries and apples. In the bowl mix together the topping ingredients. Crumble the topping mixture over the blackberries and apples.

Bake for 60 minutes or until nicely golden brown.

Blueberry & Apple Crunch

Dale remembers his mom making this on many occasions. She would make a roast of beef or meat loaf and then once she removed the main course from the oven she would pop the crunch in the oven as the oven was already hot. By the time we finished dinner the dessert would be piping hot and ready for us to eat.

1	cup	blueberries
1	cup	apples, peeled, cored and diced
1	cup	flour
1	cup	brown sugar
1/4	tsp	salt
1/2	tsp	cinnamon
1/2	cup	butter, softened

Procedure

Preheat your oven to 350°. Spray an 8" square baking dish and place blueberries and apples on the bottom of the dish to cover the bottom fully. Sprinkle the white sugar over the apples and berries.

In a bowl mix together the white flour, brown sugar, salt and cinnamon. Add the butter to the mixture and use your hands to incorporate it and create a crumble mixture.

Top the apples and berries with the crumble mixture and then pop it into a 350° oven for 30 minutes.

Blueberry Fluff

This is an easy dessert to make when you are pressed for time and is wonderful to serve at a barbecue when you are dining outside.

20	oz	can blueberry pie filling
20	oz	can pineapple, crushed and drained
14	oz	can sweetened condensed milk
8	oz	whipped topping

Procedure

In a bowl mix the pie filling, pineapple and condensed milk. Fold in the whipped topping. Pour into dessert dishes or parfait dishes and chill before serving.

Recipe Tips

Add crushed nuts or toasted coconut for additional flair.

Boiled Icing aka Seven-Minute Frosting

Your staff are top-notch, breakfast was a delight each and every day and we thoroughly enjoyed the little extras that you do – they were not overlooked. – Guest

2		egg whites
1/3	cup	cold water
1 1/2	Tbsp	corn syrup
1 1/2	cups	sugar
1	tsp	vanilla

Procedure

Put egg whites, sugar, water and syrup in top of double boiler. Beat until mixed well. Place over rapidly boiling water.

Beat constantly with electric beater while it cooks for 7 minutes or until it will stand in peaks when beater is raised. Remove from heat. Add vanilla. Beat. Fills and frosts 2 layer cake, 8" or 9".

Recipe Tips

A jar lid or a couple of marbles in the bottom half of a double-boiler will rattle when the water gets low and warn you to add more before the pan scorches or burns.

Bread Pudding

Todd has made thousands of these bread puddings. You can make it in the dish as the recipe says or individual serving dishes. This is great for dessert or breakfast.

		enough bread cubes to fill a 9″x13″ square glass baking dish
4	cups	milk, divided
2		eggs
1		package instant vanilla pudding mix
1/2	cup	raisins

Procedure

Cut up bread into 1" cubes and fill a 9"x13" glass baking dish. Then pour the cubes out of the baking dish into a large bowl and add the raisins to the bowl.

In a separate bowl mix the instant pudding mix and 2 cups of the milk for 2 minutes then let sit for 5 minutes. Now add 2 eggs and mix well. Then add 2 more cups of milk and stir well.

Pour the mixture over the bread cubes and mix to fully incorporate. Pour the mixture into the glass baking dish and bake at 350° for 50 minutes.

Recipe Tips

You can substitute the bread cubes for croissants or even brown bread with raisins.

Chocolate Brownies

1	lb	chocolate chips
6	Tbsp	butter, unsalted
3		eggs
3/4	cup	brown sugar
1 1/2	cups	flour
1 1/2	cups	walnuts, chopped
1	tsp	vanilla

Procedure

Preheat your oven to 375°. Line a brownie pan with parchment paper. Lightly spray the sides of the parchment paper.

In a bowl melt 1/4 of the chocolate chips with the butter in a bowl over a pot of hot water. Let cool slightly. In another bowl add the eggs and brown sugar and whisk. Now, whisk in the melted chocolate mixture.

Sift in the white flour and mix and then fold in the walnuts, mix in the vanilla and the remaining chocolate chips. Do not over-mix the brownie batter.

Pour the mixture into the brownie pan and spread out and then bake for 30 minutes. Cool the brownies in the pan then remove from the pan and cut into individual brownies.

Recipe Tips

A brownie isn't complete unless it is topped with wonderful chocolate icing. Our favourite chocolate icing follows:

1 cup sugar, 2 tablespoons of cocoa, 1 cup butter, 1 cup milk, 1 teaspoon of vanilla. Sift sugar and cocoa. Add butter. Add milk. Bring to rolling boil. Boil only 1 minute! Add 1 teaspoon vanilla. Pour into small mixing bowl and beat until spreadable.

By The Bay Rum Sauce

We truly enjoyed our stay and were happy to spend our three days with you as it allowed us to tour the Baccalieu Trail, the Irish Loop, as well as visit Cape St. Mary's without having to change accommodations. – Guest

2	cups	dark brown sugar
2	cups	water
1	tsp	salt
2	Tbsp	butter (no substitutes)
2	Tbsp	Screech rum (or add more to taste)
1/4	cup	cornstarch
3/4	cup	water

Procedure

Boil all together over medium high heat and thicken with a mixture of cornstarch and water. Whisk to incorporate.

Chocolate Mousse

A true highlight of our Newfoundland vacation and something not to be overlooked. – Guest

2/3	cup	chocolate syrup
1 1/4	cups	sweetened condensed milk
2	cups	heavy (whipping) cream
1/2	tsp	vanilla
1/2	cup	slivered almonds
		whipping cream for garnish (optional)
		chocolate shavings for garnish (optional)

Procedure

In a large bowl mix together chocolate syrup, sweetened condensed milk, whipping cream and vanilla. Place in fridge along with the beaters and chill well.

When the mixture is well chilled remove from the fridge and beat until it reaches high thick stiff peaks. Spoon the mixture into mousse cups, put in the freezer and freeze. Remove from the freezer 15-20 minutes before serving.

You can opt to garnish with whipped cream or chocolate shavings for nice presentation.

Cream Cheese Icing

The owners of George House offer 5 star service, 5 star comfort, and 5 star accommodations and amenities. – Guest

1/3	cup	cream cheese, softened
4	Tbsp	butter or margarine
1	tsp	vanilla
1/4	tsp	salt
2 1/2	cups	icing sugar

Procedure

In a large bowl cream the cream cheese and margarine, beat in the vanilla and salt. Gradually add the icing sugar blending and mixing all the time.

Coconut Frosting

You'll want to reserve dinner with your room as the experience in the dining room is as breathtaking as the vistas. – Guest

1	cup	coconut, flaked or shredded
1/4	cup	butter or margarine
1/3	cup	cream cheese, softened
3	cups	icing sugar
1	Tbsp	milk
1/2	tsp	vanilla

Procedure

In a dry frying pan toast the coconut and then allow to cool. This will toast your coconut.

In a bowl cream the margarine or butter and cream cheese together and then add icing sugar alternatively with milk and vanilla until beaten smooth. Add one half of the toasted coconut and mix well.

Frost your cake and then top with the remaining coconut.

Fudgey Brownies

I felt at home. This is a B&B that functions in "style" while providing the relaxing carefree vacation that all of us yearn to experience. – Guest

1/2	cup	butter
1	cup	sugar
1	tsp	vanilla
2		eggs
1/4	cup	chocolate, melted
1/2	cup	flour
1/2	cup	walnuts, chopped

Procedure

In a bowl cream together the butter, sugar, and vanilla. Beat in the eggs and incorporate well. Add the melted chocolate and then stir in the flour and walnuts.

Bake in a 8" square pan at 325° for 30 minutes.

Cool and cut into squares. These can be served as is or you can add icing to them.

Great-Aunt Mary's Steamed Blueberry Pudding

Todd remembers, "My Great-Aunt Mary would make this blueberry steamed pudding for our family at Christmastime. Great-Aunt Mary passed away and my mom continues the tradition of making this celebrated pudding for the family over the holidays. It brings back many fond memories."

2 1/2	cups	flour
1/2	cup	bacon fat
1	cup	molasses
1		egg
1	tsp	allspice
1	tsp	cinnamon
1	tsp	ginger
1	tsp	salt
1	tsp	baking soda
1/4	cup	water, hot
2	cups	blueberries

Procedure

In a bowl sift flour and spices together. In a separate bowl cream the cold bacon fat and molasses together and then beat into the mixture the egg.

In a measuring cup dissolve the baking soda into the hot water and add to the molasses mixture. Mix well.

Add the dry ingredients and beat well. Finally, fold in the blueberries being careful not to crush the blueberries. Pour batter into a mold and steam for 3 hours.

Hard Sauce

This recipe will make about one cup of hard sauce and is ideal to be served over fruitcake.

1/2	cup	butter (no substitutes)
1	cup	icing sugar
1/8	tsp	salt
1	tsp	water, hot
3/4	tsp	vanilla

Procedure

In a bowl cream butter and sugar until well combined and light. Add the salt and beat to incorporate and then add the hot water and beat. Put in a bowl and chill.

Housekeeper's Trifle

This is an easy recipe to make and it does make a great presentation when you serve it at a family dinner or bring it to a potluck event.

24		ladyfingers
4	Tbsp	sherry
1/2	cup	raspberry preserves
1 1/4	cups	raspberries
1 1/2	cups	prepared Bird's custard
1	cup	whipped cream
1/2	cup	flaked almonds
		Mint sprigs, for garnish

Procedure

Spread 1/2 of the lady fingers over the bottom of a large glass serving bowl. Sprinkle 1/2 the sherry over the cake to lightly moisten it and then spoon 1/2 of the raspberry jam over the lady fingers.

Retain all but a few fresh raspberries and make a layer of 1/2 of the raspberries. Pour 1/2 the custard to cover the first layer. Repeat all the first steps again to create second layer. Cover and chill in the fridge for minimum 2 hours.

Just prior to serving evenly layer top with sweetened whipped cream. Use mint and reserved raspberries to decorate.

Recipe Tips

There are many variations of this, including substituting sponge cake for the ladyfingers, using blueberries and blueberry jam instead of raspberry. Try making this with Frangelico instead of sherry – it's one of our favourites.

Lucy's Bread Pudding

The warm and welcoming attitude of the owners and everyone that worked at the B&B gave a glow to our visit throughout the time we spent there. – Guest

2 1/4	cups	milk
2		egg, slightly beaten
2	cups	day-old bread cubes
1/2	cup	brown sugar
1/2	tsp	cinnamon
1	tsp	vanilla
1/4	tsp	salt
1/2	cup	raisins

Procedure

In a bowl add milk and eggs and mix well. Pour the mixture over the bread cubes and stir in remaining ingredients. Pour mixture in 8" round baking dish or pie plate.

Place the dish with mixture in a large pan and pour hot water around it 1" deep. Put in oven and bake at 350° for 45 minutes. If unsure if fully cooked use a knife and insert in middle of pudding and it should come out clean.

We like to cut this into 8 pie-shaped sections and serve with a dusting of cinnamon or icing sugar and a dollop of whipped cream.

Recipe Tips

Bread pudding is popular on restaurant menus these days all over North America. Every region has its own way of making it.

Bread pudding comes from the Victorian era and was typically a Christmas dessert. This is an ideal way to use up day-old bread and is best served warm – although Dale's mom served it chilled.

Lucy's Raisin Rice Pudding

Dale remembers, "My mom made this often and it was a simple and easy dessert to make. She would serve it warm and we'd always pour a little milk on it in our dish. If there was any leftovers I'd try and make sure that I was the one to get the second helping the next day and it was just as good chilled – again with a little milk on it."

1/2	cup	rice, uncooked
4	cups	milk
1/2	cup	sugar
1/2	tsp	salt
1	tsp	lemon peel, grated
1/4	tsp	nutmeg
1/2	cup	raisins
		dab of butter

Procedure

In a bowl mix the rice, milk, sugar, and salt and then pour into a buttered ovenproof baking dish. Bake at 300° for 1 hour, stirring every 15 minutes. Add lemon peel, nutmeg, and raisins and bake for an additional 1 1/2 hours. Pudding will thicken and become creamy.

Molasses Candy

We, without hesitation, recommend this establishment to anybody travelling in the area and seeking a great experience. – Guest

1	cup	molasses
1	tsp	vinegar
1/4	cup	water
1/4	cup	butter (no substitutes)

Procedure

In a pot combine all ingredients. Bring to a boil continually stirring and then reduce to a simmer and continue to stir for an additional 10 minutes.

Drop the candy mixture by the teaspoon onto waxed paper and let cool. Wrap individually in small cut-up pieces of waxed paper.

One-Pan Brownies

Save time and cleanup by mixing and making these brownies all in one pan. I remember my mom making these and delighting in just how easy they were.

1/2	cup	butter (no substitutes)
2	cups	sugar
1	cup	flour
1	cup	pecans, chopped
4		eggs
1/2	cup	unsweetened chocolate chips
1	tsp	vanilla extract
1/4	tsp	cinnamon, ground

Procedure

Preheat oven to 350°.

Melt butter in 13"x9" baking pan in oven; remove from oven.

Stir in sugar, flour, pecans, eggs, chocolate chips, vanilla extract and cinnamon with a fork until well blended. Smooth batter with spatula.

Bake for 25-30 minutes or until wooden pick inserted in centre comes out clean. Cool completely in pan on wire rack. Cut into bars.

Recipe Tips

These make a great homemade gift idea. Cut up the squares and put them in a nice gift box or gift bag.

Quick Pumpkin Pudding

The premises were immaculate and offered comfort unrivalled on our trip through Newfoundland. – Guest

1		package vanilla pudding mix (5 oz or so)
1	can	Carnation milk
1	can	pure pumpkin (12 oz size)
1	tsp	pumpkin pie spice
		whipped cream

Procedure

Beat pudding mix and evaporated milk according to package directions in large bowl; refrigerate for 5 minutes. Add pumpkin and pumpkin pie spice; mix well. Spoon into dessert dishes. Refrigerate for 10 minutes or until ready to serve. Top with whipped cream.

Peach-A-Boo Cobbler

The culinary skills of our hosts surpassed those of any other place in which we dine in the province (you must try Dale's Bread Pudding). – Guest

1	Tbsp	cornstarch
1/4	cup	brown sugar
1/2	cup	cold water
2	cups	fresh peaches, peeled, pitted, thinly sliced and lightly sugared
1	cup	fresh blueberries
1	Tbsp	butter
1	Tbsp	lemon juice
1	cup	flour
1/2	cup	sugar
1 1/2	tsp	baking powder
1/2	tsp	salt
1/2	cup	milk
1/4	cup	butter (no substitutes), softened
2	Tbsp	sugar
1/4	tsp	nutmeg, ground

Procedure

In a pot mix cornstarch, brown sugar, and cold water and then add peaches and blueberries. Heat on stove on moderate heat until mixture thickens. Add tablespoon of butter and lemon juice. Pour mixture into a sprayed ovenproof glass baking dish.

Sift flour, sugar, baking powder and salt in a bowl. Add milk and soft butter and beat until smooth. Pour mixture over the fruit and then sprinkle 2 tablespoons of sugar and 1/4 teaspoon of nutmeg over the batter.

Bake at 350° for 30 minutes and then let cool for 15 minutes. Serve warm with whipping cream.

Recipe Tips

This recipe needs to be made with fresh peaches, not canned peaches. While you may be tempted to used canned they are softer and the recipe will not bake properly. Celebrate the harvest when you can buy a basket of fresh peaches in the store. Make this cobbler and some peach jam or a peach pie – you cannot beat the taste of a fresh peach.

Raspberry & Date Bars

A haven of Newfoundland hospitality from arrival to departure, we experienced nothing but sincere warmth and welcome of our hosts and their staff.
– Guest

3	cups	raspberries, whole (frozen or fresh)
3	cups	dates, chopped
1/4	tsp	salt
1/4	cup	water
1	Tbsp	lemon Juice

Crust and Topping

1 3/4	cups	flour
1 3/4	cups	rolled oats
1	cup	brown sugar
1/4	tsp	soda
1/4	tsp	salt
3/4	cup	margarine or butter, melted

Glaze (optional)

2 1/2	cups	powdered sugar, sifted
1/3	cups	lemon juice
1	Tbsp	butter or margarine
1/4	tsp	vanilla

Procedure

Combine raspberries, dates, and water. Cook over low heat, stirring frequently, until dates and berries blend into thick purée. Add salt and lemon juice. Remove from heat and set aside.

Crust and Topping

Combine dry ingredients. Add melted butter or margarine and stir to crumb consistency. Pour slightly more than half the crumbs into a 9"x13" pan. Pat to form firm crust.

Bake 350° for 12 minutes. Spread filling over baked crust. Top with remaining crumbs.

Bake 350° for 25-30 minutes. Cool to room temperature. Cut and serve.

Glaze

Stir together powdered sugar, vanilla, and butter or margarine.

Add lemon juice to make drizzling consistency.

St. Pierre et Miquelon Chocolate Pots de Crème

A few summers ago we had a wonderful trip to St. Pierre et Miquelon. While we didn't enjoy our "chambre d'hotes" during our visit we did enjoy all the sights and especially the food. The boulangeries were wonderful with fresh pastries and french croissants and Todd loved their pots de crème. Here is our take on this great French dessert.

1	cup	half-and-half or light cream
1/2	cup	sweet chocolate chips for baking
2	tsp	sugar
3		large egg yolks, slightly beaten
1/2	tsp	vanilla

Procedure

In a heavy small saucepan combine the half-and-half or light cream, chocolate, and sugar. Cook and stir over medium heat about 10 minutes or until mixture reaches a full boil and thickens.

Gradually stir about half of the hot mixture into the beaten egg yolks. Return all of the egg yolk mixture to the saucepan. Cook and stir over low heat for 2 minutes. Remove from heat; stir in vanilla. Pour chocolate mixture into 4 or 6 pots de crème cups or small dessert dishes. Cover and chill for 2-24 hours.

Makes 4-6 servings.

Spotted Dick

We found your service to be above reproach, and the facility in the heritage home was beautifully restored. Our visit was a memorable introduction to the charms of outpost Newfoundland. – Guest

1/3	cup	butter (no substitutes)
1/3	cup	sugar
2		eggs
1 1/2	cups	flour
1	tsp	baking powder
	pinch	salt
1/3	cup	milk
1	Tbsp	water
1/2	cup	raisins

Procedure

Cream together the butter and the sugar, before gradually adding the eggs, while beating. Carefully add the flour in small amounts along with the baking powder and salt. Beat in the water followed by milk to get a smooth creamy consistency – adjust quantities of liquid accordingly. Stir in the sultana raisins.

Transfer the mixture to a greased pudding bowl, approximately 2-pint capacity. Cover with double layer of waxed paper tied with string around the outside of the bowl and place in a large Dutch oven or similar pot with enough water to reach halfway up the exterior of the bowl. Simmer for 2-2 1/2 hours, covered.

George HOUSE

HERITAGE BED & BREAKFAST

BEVERAGES & COCKTAILS

Baccalieu Castaway

1	oz	rum
1/2	oz	coconut liqueur
1/2	oz	banana liqueur

Procedure

In a martini shaker, fill with ice and add all the ingredients. Shake well and strain into short glass with ice.

Between The Sheets

1/2	oz	gin
1/2	oz	rum
1/2	oz	Cointreau

Procedure

In a martini shaker, fill with ice and add all the ingredients. Shake well and strain into a short glass with ice.

Captain Dildo's Cocktail

3/4	oz	gin
3/4	oz	Cointreau
	dash	grapefruit juice

Procedure

In a martini shaker, fill with ice and add all the ingredients. Shake well and strain into a short glass with ice. Serve with an orange slice.

Newfoundland Codder

2	oz	vodka
4	oz	cranberry juice
	splash	lime juice

Procedure

In a martini shaker, fill with ice and add all the ingredients. Shake well and strain into a chilled martini glass. Serve with a lemon or lime twist.

Well Water

1 1/2	oz	gin
1	oz	Triple Sec
1/2	oz	Blue Curacao

Procedure

In a martini shaker, fill with ice and add all the ingredients. Shake well and strain into a short glass with ice. Serve with a lemon curl.

A Julie Dorantini

This recipe is dedicated to our friend Julie Doran from the UK. This martini is as sweet as she is and we named it in her honour.

2	oz	vodka
1	oz	Frangelico

Procedure

In a martini shaker, fill with ice and add all the ingredients. Shake well and strain into a chilled martini glass. Grate a little dark chocolate in the glass as a garnish.

Classic Martini

1 1/2	oz	vodka
1/2	oz	vermouth
1		olive

Procedure

In a martini shaker, fill with ice and add all the ingredients. Shake well and strain into a chilled martini glass. Serve with a cocktail stick of olives.

Cold Comfort Martini

1 1/2	oz	vodka
1/2	drop	honey

Procedure

In a martini shaker, fill with ice and add all the ingredients. Shake well and strain into a chilled martini glass. Serve with a lemon twist.

Dale's Dirty Martini

2	oz	vodka
1/2	oz	dry vermouth
1/2	oz	olive juice

Procedure

In a martini shaker, fill with ice and add all the ingredients. Shake well and strain into a chilled martini glass. Serve with a lemon twist and a cocktail stick of olives.

Nutty Tourist Martini

1 1/2	oz	vodka
1/2	oz	Frangelico
1/2	oz	Limoncella

Procedure

In a martini shaker, fill with ice and add all the ingredients. Shake well and strain into a chilled martini glass. Serve with a lemon twist.

Dildo Cove Martini

1 1/4	oz	vodka
1/4	oz	Gran Marnier
1/4	oz	Amaretto
1/4	oz	vermouth

Procedure

In a martini shaker, fill with ice and add all the ingredients. Shake well and strain into a chilled martini glass.

Pomegranate Martini

2	oz	vodka
1 1/2	oz	pomegranate juice
1 1/2	oz	grapefruit juice
1/2	oz	lime juice
1/2	oz	simple sugar syrup

Procedure

In a martini shaker, fill with ice and add all the ingredients. Shake well and strain into a chilled martini glass.

Todd's Cosmopolitan

3	oz	vodka
1/2	oz	triple sec
		splash of cranberry juice
		squeeze of fresh lime juice

Procedure

In a martini shaker, fill with ice and add all the ingredients. Shake well and strain into a chilled martini glass. Serve with a lemon or orange twist.

Veronica's Annapolis Valley Apple

Veronica is a lovely person from Croatia who inspired us to try this martini. We consumed many of them on New Years Eve and remember every time we enjoy one.

2	oz	Crown Royal
1	oz	DeKuyper Pucker Sour Apple
		splash of cranberry juice

Procedure

In a martini shaker, fill with ice and add all the ingredients. Shake well and strain into a chilled martini glass. Serve with a lemon twist and slice of green apple.

SPIRITED COFFEES

649 Millionaire Coffee

1/2	oz	Bailey's Irish Cream
1/2	oz	Kahlua
1/2	oz	Frangelico
		coffee, hot

Procedure

Run a slice of lemon around the top rim of a coffee cup and then rim the cup with sugar.

Pour in the coffee and then add the remaining ingredients.

Dildo Islander

1/2	oz	Frangelico
1/2	oz	rum
		whipping cream

Procedure

Run a slice of lemon around the top rim of a coffee cup and then rim the cup with sugar.

Add the coffee and then the rest of the ingredients and top with whipped cream.

Route 80 Bumpy Road

1/2	oz	Tia Maria
1/2	oz	rum
1/2	oz	Creme de Cacao
		coffee, hot

Procedure

Run a slice of lemon around the top rim of a coffee cup and then rim the cup with sugar.

Add coffee to the cup, add the remaining ingredients and top with whipped cream.

Index

C

D

E

O

P

Dale Cameron (left) and Todd Warren. Photo: H. Cole

DALE CAMERON was born in Mississauaga, Ontario, and is the entrepreneurial spirit behind Inn By The Bay and George House Heritage Bed & Breakfast, as well as a few additional tourism-related businesses. Dale has spent his whole life in sales and marketing, and while he is always coming up with new ideas for future ventures, he loves to spend time visiting with guests, cooking and enjoying a great glass of wine. He was instrumental in George House Heritage Bed & Breakfast winning ACOA's Technology in Tourism award in 2010. Dale has a secret passion for writing and is currently collaborating on a series of children's books based on Newfoundland and Labrador's historic past.

TODD WARREN, born in Dildo, Newfoundland and Labrador, is best known as innkeeper of the award-winning Inn By The Bay and George House Heritage Bed & Breakfast. Todd has spent more than 20 years in the hospitality industry. When not working he enjoys spending time baking, cooking and travelling. Todd has received many mentions in various travel publications for his culinary talents as well as being awarded the PRIDE Award by Hospitality Newfoundland and Labrador for professionalism and raising the profile of the bed and breakfast industry in Newfoundland and Labrador. This is his first foray into publishing, and he is looking forward to publishing his second cookbook.

Dale and Todd live seasonally in Dildo and enjoy the sense of community that a Newfoundland outport provides. They enjoy walking the local trails with their two miniature schnauzers, Hudson and Bridges, and spending countless hours in the kitchen testing recipes and hosting dinner parties. In the off season they spend their time travelling all over and taste testing along the way.